Dump the Junk

Mary Whiting

Dump the Junk

Design and illustrations by Ben Nash
bennash@mac.com

Printed and bound by Antony Rowe Limited, Eastbourne

ISBN 0 - 9544324 – 0 - 1

First edition February 2003

Published by Moonscape Ltd, Forest Row, England
Tel: 01342 825845
www.moonscapebooks.com

DUMP THE JUNK!

Over 300 Tips to encourage children to eat healthy food

Written and compiled by
MARY WHITING

with illustrations by Ben Nash

MOONSCAPE

ACKNOWLEDGEMENTS

I am very indebted to everyone who was kind enough to send me tips and who shared their concerns and family anecdotes. I am enormously grateful for them all. It should perhaps be said, however, that the concerns which parents expressed vastly outnumbered their tips, clearly showing the extent of the problems that parents struggle with nowadays. Many parents' comments showed an awareness and shrewd understanding of the current situation and of the issues involved. As for the tips, some were mentioned by several parents, while others appeared only once. At times I was amazed at parents' sheer inventiveness and originality, and I am delighted to be able to pass on their excellent ideas to other parents who, I hope, will find them useful with their own families.

I am also very indebted to the Food Commission's Parents' Jury for their anecdotes and for the tips they gave me when I was researching this book. The Parents' Jury is a Food Commission campaign for better quality food for children, and in which parents are given a chance to voice their opinions on various aspects of the situation. Any parent who wishes can join – indeed numbers grow all the time. For details please see page 141.

Mary Whiting
January 2003

To Mary Roe
who made such a huge
contribution to this book

CONTENTS

INTRODUCTION
- it's not your fault!

The food problems you struggle with daily are not of your making. *You* didn't create a 'children's food' market, *you* didn't dream up 'pester power', *you* didn't invent fast food, *you* didn't ask for your children to be advertised at by big business. Nor did *you* invent super-high sugar breakfast cereals or lurid, extruded bag-snacks, or laughable lunch-box food, or any of the other nutrient-depleted, processed-beyond-recognition, tooth-rotting, artery-clogging, flab-building, palate-destroying, brain-zapping glop that is marketed so seductively and so determinedly at your children....These were all someone else's ideas, so that some mighty, wealthy company could become even mightier and wealthier.

But *you* have to deal with the consequences. The purpose of this book is to offer tips and ideas to help you to feed your children the good food that is their birthright and to dump the junk!

HOW TO BE IN CHARGE

Ask any parent how easy it is to get their children to eat good, healthy food, and the answer will probably be a resounding groan. Of course, one would expect most children to prefer ice-cream to spinach, but today's parents face problems completely unknown to previous generations.

Over the last fifty years, children's eating patterns have changed dramatically – and mostly for the worse. In that time, children's consumption of biscuits has risen by four times, confectionary by 25 times and soft drinks by 34 times, while their consumption of milk, bread, green vegetables and red meat has declined. 'Fast foods' have appeared, free school milk was stopped along with good nutritional requirements for school meals, and we have seen the emergence of a completely new food category: 'children's food'. This last item is a landmark change: for the first time, children are being fed a completely different type of food to their parents.

It isn't as if these 'children's foods' are designed to be especially beneficial for children. Most are nutrient depleted, highly processed and stuffed with sugar, salt or saturated fat. Many exist solely through the liberal use of additives. But they are heavily advertised during children's television programmes, making children want them (or, rather, the packaging and 'gifts') with the result that parents are often pestered into buying them.

> "It's like having a wicked fairy godmother taking over your child – she's on TV in your living room, she's in the shops, she's everywhere, whispering into your child's ear, telling him to do the opposite of what you want him to do. Sometimes I feel it's hopeless."
>
> "What's happening is that our children are just being brainwashed."

Eating out presents similar problems. Advertised fast food is everywhere; 'children's menus' consist chiefly of fried food and processed desserts, and just getting a drink of plain water can be difficult. Arrays of 'children's' confectionary and salted bag snacks are on sale at children's eye-level in almost every type of establishment. Many parents feel that their authority is constantly undermined by the food industry, leaving them feeling sabotaged, furious and helpless. Whatever can parents do against this multi-faceted attack?

This book is a compendium of various forms of defence against advertising fallout that have been suggested to me over the years by harassed parents. Much of it is set down in parents' own words. If the tone is sometimes angry, it is because parents have been fighting in the front lines – they could be called true war correspondents!

Top Tip of all: You're in charge!

• You know more than your children about eating well. That puts you in charge. Your children's health is precious and it largely depends on YOU. (If not you, who else will bother?)

Yes, there are pressures and problems that earlier generations knew nothing of, but the bottom line is that *you* do the shopping, *you* do the menu planning, and *you* do the cooking. So at least at home, your child can eat and drink only what you have decided to provide. Even if there is poor fare at school, there can still be good food at home.

• If there is something you'd rather your children didn't have, simply don't buy it – ever. It's much easier to say 'No' to something when it's not in the house.

Start early

The younger the children, the easier it is for them to acquire the taste for and the habit of good food. With babies, feed them home prepared food, so the taste of your own home cooked food is familiar from the start. (It's also much cheaper.) Remember not to add any salt or sugar until you've taken out the baby's portion.

If children are brought up to eat good, home-cooked food from the word go, that's what they will think of as 'proper' food. Also, it will train their tastebuds, so when they encounter commercial food elsewhere, they may heartily dislike it. Actively work against letting your children become accustomed to commercial flavours.

• Don't assume in advance that your baby or child won't like something. Offer a new food from time to time over a period of weeks to give them time to get used to it. One idea with babies is to put something well-liked on the front of the spoon so that is tasted first, with a little of the new food behind it.

> "My mother *never* bought cakes, and I always noticed the difference between home made and bought cakes. Bought ones always seemed to have a strange extra taste which I didn't like, and I wondered what it was. Decades later, I still notice exactly the same odd taste and still wonder what it is. But I'm like my mother: if I want a cake, I make one. Much nicer, much cheaper – and I know what's in it."

• Feed your child nutrient-dense foods. Children's stomachs are very small, so there's no room for space-fillers – make every food justify its place! From babyhood, regularly give your children exceptionally nutritious foods such as eggs, milk, oily fish, white fish, liver (organic only: other kinds absorb too much artificial vitamin A from feedstuffs), kidney, and brightly coloured vegetables and fruit.

• As your children get older and become influenced by other children, you may feel you must compromise a bit. But don't anticipate it. On the contrary: work at having your children influence the others – it happens!

> "My four year-old is a little 'tryer' – he tries everything: olives, strong cheeses and all full-flavoured foods including dried fruit, broccoli, cabbage and swede! His friends, it seems, are not encouraged to try such things and stick to 'children's food'."

Know thine enemy

Remember, the food industry, like any business, has to sell us things to make a profit. As with any business, big profits are best. 'Pester power' can be hugely profitable: parents get pestered into buying things they wouldn't otherwise consider. Bingo!

Remember, the manufacturers didn't go into business to build the health of the nation. If your children's teeth rot after eating too many pre-sugared foods, that's *your* fault, says the industry – nothing to do with them! So be careful. Read every label. If in doubt don't. Buy only what your children need, not what big business wants to sell. The trick is to serve only what *you* think is right but, crucially, make it appealing to look at and delicious to eat.

Beware the TV!

Much of children's television programming is punctuated by a stream of adverts directly aimed at children. Advertising at children is restricted or even banned in a number of other European countries – why not here?

If your children watch commercial channels, try to watch too, at least some of the time, so you know what they've seen and so you can make appropriate comments on what is being advertised at them.

Plan your meals

• Write the week's menu for all meals, all snacks and all drinks, and then write your shopping list. Then buy only what's on the list. For those unused to doing this it can be an instructive exercise, and prove a great saving on both money and shopping time. Don't be put off by the time it takes to make the first few lists. It gets quicker as it becomes a routine – and remember you can then whizz round the shops (see chapter 7).

Teach them

• Gradually, introduce children to the various aspects of food. This can be anything from animal welfare to growing strawberries. Chat about which foods are especially good for them, and why (swat up some nutrition if you need to!). Children can be fascinated by this. Keep it straightforward, keep it light and be aware of your child's interest and attention span. With older children, talk about wider food issues – farming and the environment, food miles, packaging... whatever takes their interest.

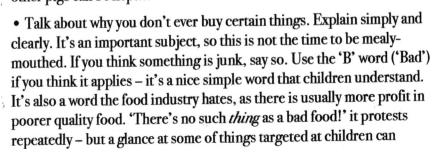

• Talk about animal husbandry when you visit a farm park. Children can be very concerned about animals being treated badly. If you pass a pig farm and see the piglets running about and playing, enjoy the sight together, and mention how other pigs can be kept...

• Talk about why you don't ever buy certain things. Explain simply and clearly. It's an important subject, so this is not the time to be mealy-mouthed. If you think something is junk, say so. Use the 'B' word ('Bad') if you think it applies – it's a nice simple word that children understand. It's also a word the food industry hates, as there is usually more profit in poorer quality food. 'There's no such *thing* as a bad food!' it protests repeatedly – but a glance at some of things targeted at children can quickly debunk that claim. A healthily sceptical view of the workings of the adult world can stand children in good stead as they grow up. If they are sceptical they'll be less gullible.

• Explain that advertisements are only about *selling*!

> **Knowledgeable children**
>
> "My children know what to eat and what's good for them, because I talk to them about it. I don't mention it much at meal times because I think that's the time for just enjoying food, but I do at other times. Now they tell me about it!"
>
> "My son (seven) was offered a ready-made, processed dessert in a carton, and he refused and said 'It's too processed!' I find that when my children are allowed a 'treat', they complain it's too sweet or too salty."

• Be enthusiastic about good foods that are on sale. Say, for example, 'Just smell this lovely ripe melon – this is the one to buy,' or 'This is the bacon to get: it's organic, so the pigs will have been properly looked after,' or 'Real bread from a real baker! Feel how heavy it is.' Let children see your joy in finding something very good as well as your disgust as seeing the not-so-good.

Involve them – early

Involving children early on is an excellent way of getting them interested in good food. A few suggestions:

• Let them grow something – anything, if it's only growing parsnip tops in water or sprouting avocado stones or onions over a jar of water. Perhaps they could sprout beans or grow radishes, or cress for the family's salads, or nasturtiums (both flowers and leaves are good in salads and for garnishes). And let them have the pleasure of harvesting their crop.

They could grow some potatoes in the ground or in a tub – *anyone* can grow potatoes! (Cook some just after you've dug them and notice the difference.) As one parent said: 'Put children in touch with the earth, the source of our food'. Let small children *play* at gardening too and pretend to make a garden using twigs and shells, even if it's just in a tub or box (and see page 38).

• Always have a few easy, perennial herbs in the garden or in tubs (chives, thyme, sage, lemon balm, mint, rosemary) for the children to smell and to rub their fingers on – and to see you using.

• Let children help in the kitchen from an early age. Cook anything with them, but cook *something*, even it's only cornflake 'cakes'. Not the healthiest option but don't worry, children almost certainly won't (a) want to eat them all, or (b) remember how many there should be left. However, if (c) they do, you have very keen children, so move quickly onto the next recipe – scones, a real cake, or something savoury.

• Encourage children's self-sufficiency. Laying the table, folding napkins, filling the water jug, pouring their own milk, buttering their bread, tossing the salad and perhaps decorating it, putting certain things away after the meal... are all suitable jobs for even quite young children, and makes them feel they have made their contribution.

• Even young children can stir, chop, slice, sieve, pour and grate, and with practice, can become quite proficient – and love it! Snipping chives or parsley for example is a pleasant job that even the youngest child could enjoy.

• Beware, especially with older children, that they don't finish up doing the dull jobs like scrubbing the potatoes. (Potatoes rarely need peeling or scraping, and taste better cooked in their skins.)

Doing their bit

"Have a few 'child-friendly' gadgets such as a garlic press. When garlic is needed I call upon my daughter. She then feels she's been part of making the nice garlic bread."

"My son will always help with a dish if his part is obvious! So he'll happily chop the parsley to scatter over the top, or grate the cheese for the topping or arrange the fruit on the plate. Well, it's a start!"

• Children can enjoy helping to weigh things, and it's especially enjoyable if you have balance scales – informal, practical mathematics!

• When you make a fruit pie, let a child make pastry decorations for the top: leaves and other shapes, balls, tassels – anything. It will probably take them ages and the pie may look a little strange but this is all fine. It was time-consuming fun. If the decorations don't get eaten, that's fine too. Making them was the thing. (Use a pliable pastry that won't crack too easily – see page 176 and 184.)

• Children can enjoy decorating a finished dish or arranging things on a plate – but allow them plenty of time. Decorations for pizza could include mushrooms, olives, salami, sardines, mild chillies, ham, peppers, anchovies ... all sliced by the children as necessary (see page 170).

• Squirting tomato sauce from a squeezy bottle over their food can be fun, and works well in getting the food eaten.

• Every year, make your own Christmas pudding with your children helping. Do it on any sunny day in autumn, so there'll be less of a problem with the steam, perhaps during the autumn half term. Everyone stirs and wishes! Also make your own mincemeat – extremely easy, and no cooking required (see pages 186 and 188).

• Older children can make whole dishes – even a whole meal. After all, ordinary home cooking is not exactly difficult. Once children are tall enough to reach the work surface and stove easily and are aware of basic food safety, many can do what most adults can.

• Children can make their own sandwiches, open or closed, from a choice of fillings, and children often eat things, and combinations of things, that they might reject if someone else had made the sandwich. One nursery school reports: "Peanut butter and banana, currants and cream cheese with celery, beetroot with cheese or cold meat, and fruit purée with cheese are all favourites".

"Let one child (I have three) be in charge of the shopping, cooking (with supervision)and presenting the meal. They really enjoy this."

"I have four children. Every weekend, one of them makes part of the dinner, either a starter, the main dish or a pudding. It's their choice what they do. My eight year-old has just started joining in. He did something very simple on toast, and of course we all ate it and said how nice it was."

"I let my two make their own nuggets out of flattened chicken breasts dipped in milk and breadcrumbs. They particularly enjoy flattening the chicken pieces by beating them with a rolling pin! Who said cooking wasn't really good fun?"

"We make delicious smoothies by liquidising frozen banana slices with fruit juice. It has a fabulous ice cream type texture and it's a great way of using over-ripe bananas. We serve it in tall glasses with cocktail straws as a treat."

Making changes

Do you need to make changes in your family's food? If so:

• A big change, such as cutting back on sweets, needs explanation at home in advance of going shopping. Find a time when you and your child are nice and cosy together and then say something like 'I've been getting very worried about all the sweets we're getting through. They only make your teeth ache and go black and rotten, and you might have to have them drilled or even pulled out, so I think we really better save sweets for just once a week'. If this makes you wince, then remember this is exactly what could happen and it will be your child that has to suffer it. (See also page 109 – 'a very sweet tip'.)

Children can be very reasonable when they feel someone has taken the trouble to explain something to them in an unhurried and friendly way. Don't be afraid of saying how a bad habit was your fault, and avoid blaming your child. You could say 'I'm sorry, I really shouldn't have let you get used to those sugary cereals. It was my fault. But from now on we'll get something better that won't spoil your teeth'.

- If you have several changes to make, stagger them over several weeks, or even months.

- Less noticeable changes, such as serving fresh fruit for dessert more often needn't be mentioned – just quietly do it.

- Try not to lecture them about it. If asked, briefly give a reason. But keep it light. Perhaps just say 'Oh I thought this would be a nice change' or 'It's too hot for fried food just now'.

Remember . . .

The responsibility for choosing the family's food is a serious matter, an adult matter, and it's yours.

HOW TO HAVE HAPPY MEALTIMES

Yes, happy mealtimes are possible, but they have to be encouraged. There are two essentials: good food and good company, and the adults can supply both. It also helps if the children feel they have a stake in the meal, as described in the previous chapter. To look at the 'good food' part first:

• You don't have to be an expert cook, but a certain level of ability is essential if you want to feed your family well – and balance the budget. Otherwise, you will be forced to depend on ready-mades and take-aways. If you wish you could cook better, it's never too late to learn, and practice makes perfect. The more you do, the quicker and the better you get.

• If your cooking isn't delicious, why should children want to eat it? 'It's not fair on them', as one mother said. 'And you're making a rod for your own back'. Be super-careful how you present 'harder' foods like Brussels sprouts (see page 48) which are one of the few foods which taste bitter – a difficult taste for children to acquire. Someone once remarked to me: 'You don't *eat* Brussels sprouts – you just push them around your plate!'

• Children are affected strongly by the smell of food, so entice your family with good cooking smells!

• Just the aroma of onions frying, the first stage in many dishes, can be enough to get people's anticipatory juices flowing. The smell of bacon cooking is almost irresistible, and bacon can go into almost anything savoury. Grilling a little pâté on toast also makes a good smell.

• Toasted teacakes have a wonderful 'tea-time' aroma: if you can, toast them by the fire with your children. Delicious with butter and Cheddar cheese as a winter tea-time treat.

- Have other 'hearth-rug' or 'rainy-day-picnics' on the floor for variety and fun.

- If you're out all day, make a slow-cooked dish that simmers away all day, and is ready in the evening with its wonderful aromas – and with almost nothing extra for you to do before you eat (see page 168).

"My mid-week routine is simple: each evening I get the next day's dinner (usually a one-pot dish) prepared and put in its pot in the fridge. Next morning, the pot goes into the oven on a very low heat and when we all come home, the dinner's ready – and the whole house smells wonderful. The children are instantly hungry, and it's a great 'welcome home' to everyone especially on a cold winter evening. Also, if the older one has to eat early and rush out, he can help himself to a proper dinner before he goes."

"My biggest helper is my enormous pressure cooker – it's stainless steel, 20cm (8") high and is shaped like a witch's cauldron, which is what we call it. It makes massive amounts of soup, stews and stock, so it's easy to mass-produce things, and so quick. It's also great for spinach which needs a big, stainless steel pan. I've even made marmalade in it. *And* it looks good on the table! Not cheap, but it's indispensable." (See page 141.)

- Let everyone help themselves from serving dishes in the middle of the table (see page 27) as your general rule.

- Of course, you will sometimes want to make an individual dish with special visual appeal for a young child, although it won't hurt the rest of the family if the whole dish of mashed potato sometimes comes with a face on it made out of tomato pieces!

Quick decorations can be added to other family dishes – a criss-cross of chive blades, twists of lemon, a little flag, black grapes or other small fruits all round the edge of a dish, or arranged in a domino pattern.

• Anything with a golden topping looks appetising. Grated cheese mixed with a few breadcrumbs sprinkled over a dish and then grilled can make the world of difference.

• In general, when preparing or adapting a dish for a child, the rule is 'the smaller (i.e. younger) the child, the smaller the pieces of food'. Adults and older children may enjoy chewing big chunks, but young children delight in little pieces: very small new potatoes, a tiny heap of peas, matchstick carrots, a small drumstick to eat as finger food, small triangles or fingers of bread, a bread roll cut into slices, small radishes, satsumas, paper thin slices of cucumber and tomato, tiny florets of cauliflower or broccoli, seedless grapes, the smallest apples and so on.

• Imaginatively presented food can make the difference between acceptance and refusal, especially with younger children. Produce surprises, bright colours (natural, not dyed!!) and make simple patterns. Paint a face on the shell of the boiled egg. Make faces (smiley faces, clowns, teddies, animals, a favourite story book character) with a tomato or carrot nose, cucumber eyes, a sausage smile, spooky radish teeth, shredded lettuce/cabbage/carrot hair, 'rabbit' ears made from two cos lettuce or chicory leaves ... the possibilities are endless. If your child responds to this, look in the library for books with other ideas.

> " At a buffet, I saw a dish of cream cheese decorated with long chive blades and cucumber slices to look like a noughts-and-crosses game! I immediately decided to copy that idea at home."

• Children can enjoy eating food from small containers: use ramekin dishes, egg cups, scallop shells, coffee saucers or any small ceramic or brightly coloured bowls. Perhaps buy a few cheaply from a charity shop.

• Bake a mini-shepherd's pie for a small child in a ramekin dish. Make a batch and freeze. Similarly bake individual fruit crumbles.

• Serve one food inside another: put a few peas inside a very small lettuce leaf; put the tomato sauce inside a scooped out tomato or a half a small yellow pepper; scoop out vegetables, cook and stuff. Make cucumber and celery boats and sail on a sea of shredded lettuce. Scoop out a little cake and fill with fruit.

• Names matter! The name Bubble-and-squeak can get the sprouts eaten without a child realizing they were even there. A meaty stew can be Wolf Stew (see page 162), a heap of carrot sticks Bonfire Night Carrots, or Brussels sprouts Footballs. Make up some names with your children's interests in mind, and let children make up some of their own although these may sound less than appetizing: some I've heard of include 'caterpillars' (celery slices), 'pipes' (macaroni) 'eyeballs' (pieces of hard-boiled egg), 'dead flies' and 'mouse droppings' (raisins or currants).

Give them time (lots)

"When I was a boy I guzzled absolutely everything, except okra – 'ladies' fingers' – because it was so slimy. Fortunately, my mother didn't try to make me. Years later, when I tried it in an Indian restaurant, I discovered that it wasn't slimy at all, and that I liked it! I realized that my mother's okra had been completely over-cooked. I still wouldn't want to eat it the way she did it."

"As a child I couldn't bear the thought of raw oysters. But when I grew up and I went to functions where everybody else was eating them I ate some too. It would have been too gauche not to. They weren't bad – and eventually I came to adore them."

Serving the meal: a tip from professionals

At meal time, put the food on the table in (heated) serving dishes for everyone to help themselves. Some nursery schools do this, even with children as young as two, that is as soon as a child is physically able to do so. The nurseries report that children 'eat better' than when someone else puts food onto their plates, and also that they eat more of what the nurseries describe as 'good' food. A few rules make it work well for everyone:

Each person can choose the amount they prefer of anything on the table at that time, but with the essential rule of 'fair shares'. *No one can choose to have every strawberry on the cake! Children have a great sense of justice and quickly see the fairness of this. If someone wants the topping but not the underneath – fine: but what they can't have is anyone else's share of the topping.*

Importantly, no substitutions except bread, cheese and fruit: this is the meal, and nothing else is available until the next meal, except a drink. (When children are new to this routine, allow them one or two mistakes. But tell them when your firm deadline is.)

For parents, this means that all the food should be 'good' food, so whatever the child chooses is good. If you want to restrict something, put out just a tiny amount.

Fairness aside, no criticisms are allowed about what or how much someone has taken. This seems to have a relaxing effect on children and has often solved the problem of picky eaters. Of course, normal (non-pointed) remarks on how delicious the food is are excellent.

Of course, children sometimes help themselves to too little (but they can have more) or to too much (as adults do sometimes), but by the age of four, most children can assess fairly accurately how much they can eat.

In general, this method is seen as helping children to become more socially aware and more independent, allowing and encouraging them to take responsibility for their actions. (It's also a brilliant introduction to early mathematics!)

If you are new to this way of doing things, introduce it as a nicer, more 'grown-up' way of eating – the way people eat in some restaurants or at a buffet. Tell them when it will start ('Next Sunday').

Keep it happy, keep it light

• Try to avoid leaving a child, especially a young child, to eat on their own. Apart from physical difficulties, including choking and spillages, children tend to eat less well when left to eat solitarily. Especially with young children, sit with them and chat, and also eat a little of what they are having, helping yourselves from a serving bowl or dish, even if your own meal is later. They will enjoy the meal more, eat more and learn about eating as a sociable activity.

• Aim to eat as a family at least once a day, or with as many members as can be around. Early evening may be the best time: eating close to bed-time can stop children settling down easily, and prevent them wanting much breakfast the next morning (see page 88). Prepare the meal as much as possible beforehand – even the evening before. If once a day is difficult, aim for once a week: some busy families say they make a point of having Sunday lunch all together. But, very importantly:

• Declare mealtimes a grumble-free zone. Meals should be enjoyable, so keep complaints and criticisms out. It is up to the adults to set the tone and make the rules of acceptable behaviour.

• Beware of using family mealtimes as a means of proving your authority. Fathers can be especially culpable! If there is a lecture to give, choose another time.

• Dinner time is not the time for heavy talk of nutrition and so on. Good food is for *enjoying*. While you're eating, concentrate on the pleasure of it.

Miserable mealtimes (1)

"The very best mealtimes with my family were the ones where we did all the things that modern dieticians and sociologists say you shouldn't! When we were around the table it was awful, and when we ate off our knees in front of the telly it was fine. And we ate everything on our plates without fussing because we had something to gawp at rather than fight.

My mother was (and is) a fantastic cook, but the food was often a source of niggles because my three brothers and I bickered. When we sat around the table, the food and the bickering was the focus. In front of the telly, we were all much better behaved because we had the characters on telly to focus on and chat about and share jokes about. So it was a much more comfortable, shared, social occasion."

Miserable mealtimes (2)

"I once ate dinner with a family with two teenage children. Throughout the entire meal, the girl picked on her slightly younger brother who said almost nothing, and neither parent made any attempt to stop her. It was extremely unpleasant, and I spent the whole meal wondering whether to tell her off myself. That poor boy! Was this their common mealtime pattern? Did the parents *ever* intervene?"

Miserable mealtimes (3)

"Family dinner times were always hard work because my father insisted upon serious conversation throughout. We always had to discuss something seriously. My mother's food was terrific (she became a professional) but it was completely overshadowed by the slog of having to measure up to my father's exacting standard of conversation."

• It's only reasonable to let children know in advance how long they've got before the next meal so they don't feel interrupted and resentful. For example, give a fifteen-minute and a two-minute warning. It helps, too, if meals are at a predictable time each day.

• If your meal time clashes with a favourite TV programme you're asking for trouble.

> " My three teenagers are too embarrassed to eat wisely when with their friends, so home mealtimes are a great pleasure!"

• Never underestimate the impact of an attractively laid table, with flowers – and perhaps candles (or night-lights in little saucers of water) on dark evenings – for creating a good mealtime atmosphere. Children often love arranging flowers in a little pot for the table.

• Food does seem to taste better out of doors and children often eat more outside, so use warm summer weather for 'picnic' meals when you can.

• Never try to make children eat more than they want (perhaps because the meal is the fruit of your labours?). Getting into a pattern of eating more than they need destroys children's natural sense of satiety and may lead to a habit of over-eating. Forget 'the starving millions,' etc., – all quite meaningless to a child. 'Just one more spoonful' and 'Just finish that last bit' are miserable things for a child to hear and set the stage for confrontation. Ditch it all and enjoy your meal.

As for 'waste', look round any restaurant and see how much food people leave on their plates. (Do these diners tell their children not to 'waste food'?)

> "When I was a school cook I remember a rather fierce headmaster who insisted on 'all clean plates'. He got them. But he didn't see what we saw: there was food down the back of the radiators, it went out of the window, under the tables... We didn't say anything."

• Similarly, forget about 'no pudding unless you've eaten your vegetables'. It may work once or twice, but overall, children don't see the point (what *is* the point? Your pudding is good nutritious food, isn't it? If not, why not?). It's also counter-productive: it makes the pudding more desirable and vegetables less so. Would you say 'You can't play outside unless you've done a painting first.'? You can imagine a child's complete bewilderment. Further, if you kept on saying it, the chances are the child would like painting less and less.

• You could possibly say 'Just one taste,' of a new food. They might be willing if they know they won't be urged to have any more if they don't like it. But even so, don't push it.

• Children's tastes change over time. If you haven't made an issue out of a particular food, it may well be eaten and enjoyed later on. Always have bread, cheese and fruit available in case something you serve is disliked – but allow no other alternatives.

• Children almost always recoil from slimy food. Gelatinous sauces, over-cooked vegetables, some shell-fish, gristly meat, sago and badly cooked or tinned milk puddings seem to be the chief culprits. If your child dislikes any of these, perhaps the texture could be the reason. If so, change your cooking method or forget that food. (How do you feel about eating something slimy?)

• It has been shown that if children are not feeling relaxed and happy while they eat, they digest the food less efficiently and it actually does them much less good. So forcing that extra Brussels sprout down them might not have quite the benefit you'd hoped for.

Forcing them

"My mother made me eat broad beans in parsley sauce. It was awful. I can now eat very small broad beans, but even the thought of parsley sauce makes me shudder."

"Once, when I was about ten, my father made me eat a raw oyster. He made me put it in my mouth and then kept saying 'Swallow it! Swallow it!' until I'd swallowed it. It was *revolting*. Recently, when we were having a big argument, I reminded him of it and I told him, truthfully, 'I have never forgiven you for doing that to me."

"In a restaurant, a friend asked me what *sauce Chasseur* was, and if it had any tomato in. I said I thought it had, and so he ordered something else. Why? Because, he said, his mother used to make him eat tomatoes, which he hated, so he'd made up his mind never to eat any again to 'show' her. And now, quite middle-aged, he was still 'showing' her. "

"My mother always made me eat lots of salad. It was OK but boring. I don't eat it much now. I *thought* she said it was good for my morals, which puzzled me. Looking back, I think I'd confused 'morals' with 'bowels'."

Tantalizing them

" Recently, I went into a school to do a fruit-and-veg-tasting day. I put out pieces of raw fruit and vegetables and invited the children to taste. The first class came in and they all spat out the radishes! So when the next class came in, I put the radishes to one side. What happened next went something like this:

'What are those?'

"They're radishes We're not having those.'

'Why not?'

'Because you won't like them. We're not using them.'

'But we might like them!'

'You won't.'

'But we might!'

'You *won't*! Nobody in the other class liked them at all.'

'Well *we* might like them! Why can't *we* try them?'

'Because you *won't like them*!'

'But we *might*!

'Oh, all right then, have them. But you won't like them...'

Every radish was eaten! Not one was spat out. They knew they had won. I knew I had won. Everyone was happy. Motto: if you want children to eat something, make them *demand* it!"

• Remember, no single food is essential. It can take several tastings (six to eight, usually) for someone to enjoy a new food, so produce an unfamiliar food just occasionally and in small quantities and along with other foods, so it has a chance of being accepted. If a child really doesn't like something, don't push it – no one likes everything. If you become determined about it, you'll spoil the meal for everybody, and possibly cause the child to hate that food forever.

And drinks?

• It is not essential to drink with meals, as there is plenty of water in food, especially fruits and vegetables. Nevertheless, put a water jug and glasses out, to cultivate the idea that water is the normal drink to have when you are thirsty. Diluted fruit juice is also suitable for mealtimes (only) so its acid and sugar is buffered by the food.

• If the adults want wine, put that out too, perhaps allowing older children to have small sips, or put a splash of wine into their water glasses as happens in many European countries. Overall, it gives a useful message about civilized drinking, and it can make children feel that they are now being seen as 'growing up'. Much better than the usual, heavily sweetened 'cordials'.

• At tea time, tea is fine for children as long as it is very weak. Just a splash of your tea topped up with hot water, with plenty of milk and no sweetening makes a good hot drink for a child.

• At breakfast and supper time, a hot '*café crème* (see page 87) is a useful hot drink.

• The rest of the time, plain water or milk is all you need offer. If your tap water tastes of chlorine, fill some jugs or bottles with water and leave overnight loosely covered for the chlorine to evaporate. (Even your coffee will taste better!)

Be flexible

• Adult mealtimes have about five hours between them, which is much too long for a child. Provide snacks (fruit, vegetable sticks, soup, toast, bread, unsweetened oat biscuits, or a scone) or bring a meal forward.

• If a child is hungry but there's only an hour or so before the next mealtime, provide something to tide them over. An hour is a long time to be hungry, even for an adult. It's an age for a child.

• Be prepared to be flexible about which foods to serve when. A young mother made this comment to me: 'The other morning I had a cup of coffee. But then I felt I needed something more, so I had an apple – and then I wanted something more, so I made a sandwich. And then I thought 'I've just eaten my usual lunch backwards!' Later, I thought 'if my daughter had asked for her lunch backwards, I probably would have said no, you must have the sandwich first'. We make rules for children but not for ourselves. We say 'eat it up, don't waste it', but *we* only eat as much as we want'.

'But I'm starving Mum!'

"If I told my mother I was hungry and 'couldn't wait' for the next meal, she would say 'Well, come and help me do it, and then it will be ready sooner.' So I would help, and perhaps the meal was actually ready a bit sooner – and perhaps I nibbled a bit along the way!"

" My son would often ask for a snack before dinner because he was '*starving*'. I would give him something but would always say 'You won't want your dinner, you know.' One day, he sighed and said 'Mum, have you *ever* known me not want my dinner?' and I had to admit I never had."

"My mother used the opportunity of my always being hungry at mealtimes to give me an unfamiliar food first. I was so hungry I was willing to try it – later on in the meal I might have refused it. This way she expanded my repertoire from quite an early age."

"When my two come home from school, they're ravenous, so I always have bags of fruit ready and they gobble it up. They don't want it any other time, but this way I know they have a big helping every school day."

*"But wheat and sugar **are** vegetables, Mum!!"*

HOW TO GET CHILDREN TO EAT VEGETABLES

> " My daughter's friend who came for a meal said 'I don't eat vegetables, they give you wind.' My daughter replied 'No they don't, they give you vitamins.'

Getting children to 'eat their vegetables' – or even to 'eat anything green' – seems to be a major problem for many parents. Parents worry about it not only because of the mealtime drama it can cause but also because they know that vegetables are an important component of a healthy diet. It is generally agreed that much ill-health (particularly cancer) can be avoided if we eat more vegetables and fruit. As well as fibre, these provide good quantities of vitamins A, C and E, which fight off the dangerous 'free-radicals' that allow cancers to develop.

Official advice to eat at least '5 portions of fruit-and-vegetables a day' applies to both children and adults, and although getting children to eat fruit is often easier, vegetables are often a more concentrated and valuable source of nutrients. And if vegetables are missing from a meal, what will replace them? More potato? More pudding? Or nothing – except the snack demanded by a hungry child soon afterwards?

That this problem exists, however, is in some ways not surprising. As a nation, we don't deal with vegetables at all well, and 'English vegetables' (i.e. boiled to death) are an international joke. We must all be familiar with mushy cabbage, bullet peas and soggy sprouts, dropped onto our plates in unadorned, challenging heaps.

In addition, the varieties of most vegetables – and salads – on sale nowadays are grown for the convenience and profit of producers and retailers rather than for flavour. Disease resistance, crop yield, uniformity, transportability and general cosmetic appearance all come ahead of taste and variety. Tomatoes (although botanically a fruit) are a notorious example: although attractively bright red and well-formed, they tend to have tough, acidic skins and sour, watery flesh, and the taste can be downright nasty. The cook can be hard pushed to make a decent (let alone enticing) dish out of such poor produce.

Nevertheless, I have been able to collect many ingenious recipes and tips from inventive and determined parents. The best tip of all is, of course, to grow your own vegetables: you then know they are freshly picked, you know the exact method of cultivation and, as experienced gardeners will tell you, you know how exquisitely delicious they are. And how else will you ever be able to get hold of carrots the size of your little finger that hardly yet taste of carrots, just of sweet lusciousness, or unbelievably sweet baby beetroot, or young runner beans that cook in five minutes? Also, unlike some city children who think vegetables come from the freezer, your children will know precisely where they come from, and might even have helped to grow them. What child can resist pulling pea pods off the vine, popping them open and munching the sweet and flavourful little peas inside? Almost too good to be cooked!

> "One of my recent pleasures was discovering a row of peas completely stripped, and a happy green-faced smile staring up at me at the end!"
>
> "My son wouldn't touch peas until we grew our own, and he prefers them raw."

Want to try growing your own?

Some vegetables are very easy, and almost any patch of decent garden soil will do as long as it gets plenty of sun. The easiest are potatoes, sprouting broccoli, spinach beet (sometimes called perpetual spinach and much nicer than bought spinach), courgettes and runner beans.

Of course you really need a gardening book for exact methods (see page 142) – and a good spade and fork, but the following tips are essential for a decent crop:

• *Deep digging – called 'double digging'. There is no substitute for this. It's done like this: push the spade straight down into the ground (not at an angle) to the full length of the blade (one 'spit' deep) and dig out a straight-sided trench three spade blades across and as wide as one. Put the soil to one side.*

Then take your fork, and chop up the soil at the bottom of the trench to the depth of the fork prongs. You may find clay, stone or chalk down there. Leave it there.

• *Tip in some organic matter – compost, manure, or both.*

Then step back and dig another trench butting onto the first one – putting the soil you dig out into the first trench. Again, use the fork to chop up the sub-soil at the bottom of the second trench.

Move back again and dig a third trench, and so on. When you've finished, use the soil taken from the first trench to fill the last one.

NEVER let the deep-down soil (the sub-soil) come up to the surface, as it's much less fertile (and maybe not fertile at all) so won't grow anything much.

Shuffle over the soil to level and lightly tread down, then plant your crops in warm weather in spring, following the instructions on the seed packet.

• *Keep them well watered for the first few weeks, and also in any prolonged periods without rain later on.*

• *Protect from birds, cats, dogs – and most particularly, slugs and snails, and wait for your crop! (Children can enjoy hunting for slugs and snails under plants and any garden clutter.)*

• *Of course keep pulling up all weeds while they are still tiny, as they will compete with your plants for nutrients and light – and might win.*

• *Rotate your crops – grow each one in a different place each year.*

Once you've tasted your own veg, you'll be hooked!

Make compost: Save all RAW plant scraps (including kitchen waste, flowers, etc.) except seeding weeds and diseased plants, and put into a bottomless container on soil, chopping up any woody stalks roughly. Save crushed eggshells and add; put in some torn up, wetted cardboard and paper and mix up. Keep the pile a bit moist, covered with something waterproof, and keep adding stuff. After about six months, most of it will have turned into dark brown, crumbly compost.

Tips

• Cooking vegetables at the last moment retains colour, flavour, texture and nutrients. Keeping them warm does the opposite.

• Overcooking vegetables also spoils them. Cut them into small pieces and steam, boil or stir-fry for a few minutes only. Serve immediately. When children reject soggy, kept-warm vegetables they should be complimented, not made to eat the stuff.

• Fresh vegetables have a better texture and more interesting flavour than frozen or tinned ones.

• To store carrots and green vegetables so they stay fresh and crisp: wrap them in a brown paper bag or in newspaper and moisten well under the cold tap; wrap in a plastic bag and put in the fridge. The damp paper keeps the food moist and the plastic stops the paper drying out. Brilliant for crisping up lettuces and for stopping carrots from going soft. Nicer food, less waste.

• If you don't grow vegetables, make sure that children have a chance to see raw, unprepared vegetables (and fruit). Let them hold them, cut them up, smell them and so on. When they are familiar with them and curious about them, they are more likely to try them. Some children don't even realize that potatoes are dug out of the ground, covered with earth!

• Going to a pick-your-own farm for some of your vegetables can be educational and enjoyable.

• Getting a regular delivery of organic 'box scheme' vegetables can be an event: what's in the box this week?

• At dinner time, put at least two kinds of vegetables into warmed serving dishes and let everyone help themselves.

• Put very large spoons on the table for serving the vegetables – kitchen cooking spoons rather than normal table spoons, so that one spoonful is a good helping.

> "For serving vegetables, I bought two enormous catering-size spoons from an Indian shop, and doubled my children's vegetable consumption! By contrast, I put out a very small spoon for serving pudding (see page 60). My children, aged 8 and 10, have never questioned the difference in spoon sizes. They think those are the normal sizes to have."

• If you do put vegetables directly onto a child's plate, put out very tiny amounts of different coloured ones, and arrange attractively. Larger amounts can look overwhelming and the result may be that none gets eaten at all.

• Serve a wide variety of vegetables, including less obvious ones. Include asparagus and sprouting broccoli in season (spring), kabocha pumpkin, butternut squash, aubergines, pak choy. Serve chestnuts in winter (see page 154) with Brussels sprouts.

• Brightly coloured vegetables are more attractive: red, yellow and orange peppers, sweet corn, pumpkin, squash, beetroot, roasted tomatoes, carrots, purple sprouting broccoli, thin green beans.

• Onions are nutritious and their sweet taste enhances the flavour of almost any savoury dish. They need thorough cooking, so either fry them very slowly, covered, in oil-and-water or put lots into slow-cooked dishes, such as casseroles and other composite dishes, where they will seem to disappear. You could fry them very slowly until almost caramelised as a delicious vegetable. Make oniony cheese sauce (page 158). Put lots into Bolognese sauce 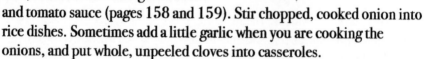 and tomato sauce (pages 158 and 159). Stir chopped, cooked onion into rice dishes. Sometimes add a little garlic when you are cooking the onions, and put whole, unpeeled cloves into casseroles.

• Sprinkle vegetables with chopped (fresh) parsley for prettiness and a lovely fresh taste. Parsley tastes sweet and is high in vitamin C.

• Put a big dab of real butter on each little mound of vegetables. (One parent insists that in her own large family this never failed to get *all* the vegetables eaten!)

> " My three year old son loves broad beans and getting them out of their pods. He loves helping in the kitchen and chopping things and making cakes."

• Serve pale green inner cabbage leaves mixed with a little darker green for an attractive colour mix. Shred the leaves, stir-fry, boil or steam lightly and serve at once tossed with freshly ground black pepper and butter. (Avoid those hard 'Dutch' cabbages which never seem to soften in cooking.)

• Vegetables as finger food can be fun. Let children eat asparagus with their fingers, dipping the spears in melted butter. Ditto the white or red stalks of Swiss chard (page 153).

• Ditto with spears of purple or white sprouting broccoli. This used to be called 'poor man's asparagus'. Lucky poor man! It's not often on sale today and only during its brief season in spring, but it's extremely easy to grow.

• Serve whole sweet corn cobs (sliced across for very young children) to eat with their fingers and with butter. Good messy fun.

• Mix sweet corn with peas and currants into rice for a popular, sweet-tasting rice dish, or try sweetcorn and pea fritters.

• If you purée vegetables such as carrots into the gravy they may very well not be noticed!

• How many different ways are there to slice carrots? Try very long sticks, thin little batons, diagonal slices, rounds, dice, or irregular chunks. Keep all the pieces small. Serve little carrots whole.

• Grow carrots and serve them lightly cooked when they are tiny – they are unbelievably sweet and mild and have a flavour quite unlike bigger carrots. Impossible to buy this taste.

• For something that looks striking and completely different, roast whole carrots with their green tops on – which of course will blacken. Serve them on a large (warm) serving plate.

• Parsleyed carrots: steam or boil carrot pieces (in chicken stock if possible) until just done. Drain. Toss in butter and lots of roughly chopped fresh parsley – or chives.

• Caramelised carrots: peel, then cut the carrots into short, thin sticks. Stir-fry in a little oil or butter until golden brown and caramelised. Delicious! Try parsnips too (see page 152).

• Cook *very* thin carrot sticks in a wok in a mixture of butter and sunflower oil, very slowly, covered, for about 15 minutes. They will be very soft, very bright orange and unbelievably sweet and delicious. Slicing them, however, takes a long time – unless you have a professional's mandolin for doing it. Almost worth getting one just for this job! It's a colossal time saver.

• Grilling vegetables keeps their colours bright.

• Make a 'bonfire'! Cut carrots and parsnips into very short very thin batons, cook and pile up into a 'bonfire' heap.

• Sometimes cook a vegetable on its own, sometimes cook it as part of a mixture, perhaps roasted (see pages 152 and 153).

• Let children help themselves but serve the vegetables first. By the time you bring the meat in, the vegetables could be eaten!

• Vary your cooking method from day to day. For example, one day serve lightly boiled broccoli and cauliflower pieces in a good cheese sauce; another day serve little broccoli florets in a mixed stir-fry; another day serve them steamed as 'trees' in mashed potato and call it a forest; another day, toss the florets in bacon fat until browned; another day put tiny half-cooked pieces in a mixed salad; another time, it can be a purée or in a soup.

• Make broccoli 'lily pads' out of thick stalks: peel the stalks, then cut across into thin slices. Eat raw or cooked as finger food or arranged on a dinner plate.

• Serve cauliflower cheese with *lots* of well-flavoured cheese-and-onion sauce, along with sauté potatoes, grilled tomatoes and bacon or ham (see page 155).

"You can get children to eat any vegetable if it's puréed into mashed potato."

"You can get children to eat any vegetable if you mix it into soups and stews with a lot of other things that they already like."

"You can get children to eat any vegetable – also a new, unfamiliar food – if it comes with a pile of really good buttery mashed potato, because that's familiar and nice."

" You can get children to eat any vegetable if it's chopped up small inside a crispy potato cake."

"You can get children to eat any vegetable if it has a big lump of real butter melting into it."

• Change the flavour of stir-fries to curry or Chinese if that's what your children like. Try adding an Indian vegetable such as okra, or, for a Chinese stir-fry, bean sprouts or tinned water chestnuts or bamboo shoots. Serve with rice.

• Change the colour of dinner! Add turmeric to your stir-fry and making it all bright yellow, thus disguising the 'green bits' very well. Frying the turmeric, rather then just sprinkling it in will stop it tasting raw and harsh.

- To make yellow vegetable rice: fry some turmeric in a little oil for a minute, then mix in a selection of cooked vegetables cut up small, and some cooked rice. Cook for another minute, stirring. For older children, add a few roasted peanuts for texture and fun.

- Some children prefer raw vegetables to cooked, so it can be a good idea to keep some around for nibbles. Try cut up carrots, celery, celeriac, red pepper, parsnip, courgette, cauliflower, broccoli. Keep a plate of them nearby while children watch television.

- Some children will eat vegetables willingly if they can 'dip' them into something. Dipping very long celery stalks can be fun. For dips, try hummus, mayonnaise or a cheese dip. Make your own dips based on a mixture of yoghurt and crème fraîche; colour with beetroot, tomato, turmeric, puréed spinach. Also try letting children dip cooked vegetables in warm cheese sauce – messy fun!

- Sometimes serve a vegetable as a purée. Purée cooked carrot or greens with a small amount of potato, a little hot milk and butter. Pack a green purée into a rectangular dish and call it a football field. Make goal post shapes with carrot sticks.

- Purée vegetables as above, but make purées of different colours, for example orange-red (carrot, pumpkin), green (broccoli, sprouts, spinach, cabbage), pink or purple (beetroot), yellow (parsnip, swede, or perhaps sweet potato on its own). Make into little patties to freeze. At meal time, serve three different coloured patties, arranged on a small plate, perhaps with parsley sprigs.

- For 'sunshine ripple' or 'rosy ripple' mash: purée cooked carrot, butternut squash, swede or beetroot and marble into mashed potato in stripes to look like 'ripple' ice-cream.

> "When my children were little, I always put cooked greens or carrots through the liquidizer and stirred it in to mashed potato so the potato looked pretty, and there was never any trouble with them over eating their vegetables."

• Sometimes make a vegetable soup. Endless variations.

• Children like stuffed vegetables – the mounded shape, especially with a golden crust, seems to attract them. Stuffed tomatoes, aubergines, peppers and marrow all work well. Courgettes are useful because they are small – and look for yellow ones for prettiness. Stuff, for example, with minced meat, onion, rice, tomato, tomato ketchup, thyme and sage – plus the chopped up bits you gouged out, and serve with an onion-and-cheese sauce (pages 158 and 164).

• Similarly, stuff a vegetable as above but very well hollowed out, and put the two halves back together again. If this doesn't hold much filling, have 'seconds' of filling ready. Children can give themselves 'refills'.

• Children like surprises, so wrap food in parcels. Wrap a filling, such as above, in any green leaves. Lightly blanch the leaves first to make them pliable. Tie up with raffia and make a bow, or secure with a toothpick.

• Combine vegetables in composite dishes such as lasagne, moussaka, meat and vegetable stews. Make lamb Nimoise with aubergines, tomatoes, onions, fennel, carrots, potatoes and garlic (page 166).

• The skins of tomatoes are usually the least delicious part, but can easily be removed. To do this put the tomatoes into a bowl and cover with boiling water. Leave for 10 seconds. Put into a sieve and hold briefly under the cold tap to set the skins, and you should be able to remove the skins easily. (Save the hot water in case you need to replace a stubborn tomato for a few more seconds.)

• Surreptitiously sprinkle un-sweet tomato slices with a very little caster sugar and the merest speck of salt and black pepper – and they will be eaten! Or try sweetening tomatoes with a drop of balsamic vinegar. Perhaps scatter finely chopped parsley and/or chives on top.

• Roasted tomatoes are something else again. Roast them whole, dribbled with a little olive oil, at your oven's lowest setting. Leave them for at least two hours, although large tomatoes can take twice as long. Or roast in a hot oven, top shelf, for 45 minutes. Either eat straightaway, or slightly warm, or cold.

• Tinned tomatoes are useful and cheap, so use lots: make quantities of thick tomato sauce and serve on toast or over pasta, rice, fish, chicken, lamb, pork, baked beans or as a pizza topping (see page 158).

• Using lots of fresh tomatoes in ratatouille gives it a brighter colour. Add a dash of ketchup and serve with rice and almost any kind of fish or meat or cooked beans.

• Home-grown tomatoes are delicious. Gardeners Delight or Sweet 100 are sweetest. Try some yellow tomatoes for fun and flavour.

• Scrumptious summer treat: serve a mixture of summer vegetables (baby carrots, peas, broad beans, runner beans), home grown if possible, with new potatoes and bacon. Toss all the vegetables in bacon fat and eat with nothing else.

> "My son loves broad beans and was introduced to them by helping to take them out of their pods"
>
> "My daughter (ten) enjoys pulling peas from our garden and knows which ones to pull and which to leave. Then she shells them – and eats quite a few!"

• Greek style beans: boil some broad beans into just soft. Grill some bacon, chop it up, and toss the beans in a little of the fat and serve mixed with the bacon pieces. The bacon counteracts the dry taste of the beans. If children want to, let them squirt the beans out of their grey cases for an even better taste.

• Golden toppings: Sprinkle grated cheese and breadcrumbs over cooked vegetables and grill to golden brown. Anything with a golden topping looks enticing.

• Cooking mange-tout peas in water makes them soggy. Instead, stir-fry them (whole, diagonally sliced) in a little oil until bright green, crisp and just cooked through.

• Brussels sprouts: when almost done, drain, then roll about in a little real butter, lemon juice and a little fresh black pepper This counters the bitter taste. Perhaps stand them on mashed potato as 'baby cabbages growing in a field'. Slice raw sprouts into thin sticks and mix into a salad.

• Red cabbage is a fantastically good winter dish. Cooked with apples and onions, its rich red juice flavoured with orange, nutmeg, brown sugar and wine vinegar, it's sweet enough, colourful enough and uncabbage-y enough to appeal to children. Served with top quality sausages it's a real winter treat. The best recipe I've found is in The Robert Carrier Cookbook (see page 143). This book has a great collection of many other delicious and inventive vegetable dishes.

• Bubble and squeak: mix chopped cooked green vegetables (especially Brussels sprouts) into mashed potatoes, and fry in bacon (or any) fat, turning once (see page 156). While you eat, talk about why it's called bubble and squeak. Is the bubble the boiling part and the squeak the frying part?

• Parsnip sweets: slice evenly into rounds, parboil, drain on kitchen paper, then fry in a little real butter and caster sugar until golden brown, turning once. A great favourite.

• Remember the pleasure of parsnips (and other vegetables) roasted around the meat! Many children enjoy a roast dinner.

• Frozen peas: throw into fast boiling water and cook for one minute. Cover, turn out the heat and leave for six minutes. Drain. Eat with butter and fresh chopped parsley or mint. 'Petits Pois' are nicest.

• Red and green peppers: red are sweeter and have more vitamin C. Stir-fry them to lightly cook only. If they develop a skin, or if the green ones turn greyish, they're overdone and will be unpleasant to eat. Or steam them, stuff them and cover them in cheese sauce (see pages 158 and 164).

• Celery boats: fill short strips with curd cheese mixed with some finely chopped raisins and some spring onion.

• Mix baked beans with finely shredded beetroot and some of its cooking juice: purple beans! Or heat the beans with chopped tomato.

• It is possible to make your own baked beans. Soak dried haricot beans overnight, drain, and cook them in fresh water. Then mix with tomato sauce. Perhaps cook finely chopped carrot, onion and celery along with the beans, too. This makes a good vegetable dish to serve with lamb.

• It can make life easier if children don't see the pudding until they've finished their main course!

And spinach? Some children love it, but many don't, and dislike the way it sets their teeth on edge. You can make it nicer by mixing in some raisins or currants and perhaps some toasted almonds or pine nuts, and a few drops of balsamic vinegar will make it taste much less acidic. But don't get hung up on it – it's only one vegetable out of many, and although it's high in calcium and iron, it's also high in oxalic acid which prevents much of these minerals being absorbed. You could try Swiss chard instead – it's similar, but less acid. Cook the stalks separately like asparagus and serve with butter, perhaps as finger food (page 153). But if your child doesn't like spinach, just forget it.

What about salads?

The chief ingredient in most salad ingredients (lettuce, cucumber, cress, celery) is water, and as salads also take up a lot of stomach space they are excellent for slimmers. For children and adolescents, however, who need maximum amounts of nutrients during this time of rapid growth, the value of salads is limited and, perhaps because of all the chewing, children are usually not keen on them anyway. Cucumber sticks can be an exception however: some babies and young children like them as finger food and seem to find them refreshing.

Apart from tomatoes, avocados and beetroot, which are more nutrient-dense, salad items are probably most useful in getting other foods eaten. For example, they can moisten a sandwich, and some children will eat a small side salad along with their pizza or lasagne. But regard salad as an adjunct to the meal, not the meal.

> "I always put out a big bowl of salad and give everyone a salad bowl, whatever we are having for dinner. My three children automatically help themselves to a bit of salad. It's just what we've always done."
>
> "My mother was French, and we always had a little salad after the meat course as a palate refresher before the cheese and fruit, which we also always had. It was very simple, usually just a few leaves and fresh herbs, but always beautifully dressed with a good olive oil dressing. I think it's a good habit."

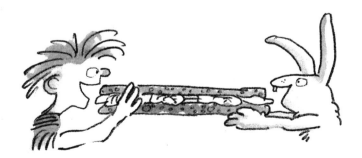

HOW TO GET CHILDREN TO EAT FRUIT

T his is usually less difficult than getting children to eat vegetables. Overall, fruit is sweeter, juicier, easier to eat raw, easier to eat a small amount at a time, comes in brighter colours – and usually it's not green.

Also, as a society, we have given fruit a better image. We view some fruits, such as strawberries, cherries, peaches, even apples sometimes, as treats, and we do not pile hot mounds of (possibly over-cooked) fruits onto children's plates and tell them to eat-it-up-it's-good-for-them the way we do with vegetables. We have allowed fruit to have a more pleasant, optional, even slightly frivolous air. Strawberries aren't *good* for us – they're a *treat*! Any 'goodness' is entirely incidental and virtually never gets mentioned. All in all, it's perhaps not surprising that children prefer fruit to vegetables.

Nowadays, however, the sweetness in fruit has a powerful rival: refined sugar. Children are bombarded with it – it seems to be put into almost anything. It's in most breakfast cereals, fruit yoghurts and fromage frais, biscuits and other bakery goods, soft and fruit-juice drinks, baked beans, ketchup ... and of course sweets and chocolate.

Once a child's palate has become accustomed to the intense sweetness of refined sugar – and also to the intense flavour of artificial sweeteners – it is much harder for them to notice the more gentle and natural sweetness of fruit. So if you want your children to enjoy fruit, the first thing is to restrict sugared (and artificially sweetened) foods, especially confectionary (see page 109).

The other particularly good thing to do is to grow fruit! Of course everyone can't do this, but some fruits take up very little growing space and are very easy for amateurs to get a crop from. There's nothing quite like home-grown, just-picked, ultra-fresh fruit, and children can enjoy picking it. It's also educational for children to *see* how fruit grows and what the parent plant looks like (and see page 39- 40):

A red currant bush is less than a metre in height and spread and couldn't be simpler. Pruning isn't essential, it's thornless and will last ten years or more. Your biggest job is covering the ripe red berries with an old net curtain or something to keep the birds off. Unlike other soft fruits, the ripe berries can hang on the bush for weeks and just get redder, riper and sweeter. Children can easily pick them. Put out sprigs of fruit to eat with bread and butter so children can pull the fruit off the stalks with their teeth, or put them into a fruit salad or jelly where they will gleam like jewels.

Raspberries are easy. Tie the metre-high stalks (canes) up to something – anything, pick the fruit and keep the birds off. At the end of summer, cut the canes that fruited down to ground level and tie up the new green ones which will fruit next year. Easy for children to pick.

Loganberries can be grown like raspberries.

Wild strawberries will grow almost anywhere, even in shade, and will spread. Children can enjoy looking under the leaves for the hidden berries.

Blackberries will also grow anywhere but need tying up. They're thorny, but the fruit is still easy for older children to pick. Just cut any briars back that are getting too long for their allotted space.

Most fruit trees can have problems with diseases and pests, but a native quince is pretty immune – and you get white blossom in spring. The quinces are too sour to eat raw but you can make them into jelly or cook them with apples, and your children will still have the experience of observing the yearly cycle of a fruit tree.

Also, a damson plum tree is small, tough and can thrive on total neglect, although some varieties are very tart and need to be made into jam or stewed with sugar. Cook a few with peaches and see the whole dish turn bright purple-red. Hunt for a sweet kind that can be eaten raw.

You could try an apple, pear or a Victoria plum tree, but you need to have an airy, open site and land that is well drained. You will need a self-fertile kind unless there are other similar trees nearby. Who knows, you might be very lucky indeed!

Strawberries grow well in tubs – and can produce lots of fruit. Protect from birds and slugs.

" When my children were little we were very hard up, but we got very good at finding free fruit. We picked up *lots* of apples – and a few plums – that had fallen off people's trees onto pavements and into hedges. We picked brambles that were growing in people's neglected hedges and on waste ground, and we even found wild raspberries in one place. One year we picked wild rosehips and made rosehip jelly, and we always picked up crab-apples that fell off a street tree and made crab-apple jelly. And this was in London! We used to say 'free fruit tastes sweetest!'"

"The best pears I ever ate fell off a huge old tree onto the grass and the hedge at one end of a little public garden. They were enormous! No one else seemed to be picking them up, so we did. We cut off the bruised bits and ate the rest with gusto. I just wish I could buy pears like that – I've never tasted anything like them."

"Every summer, we pick mulberries off big mulberry trees in a little local park. Mulberries are delicious, and the children love getting their hands bright red with the juice. I never see anyone else picking them – and it's free food!"

Tips:

• Make fruit the daily meal-ending, but avoid letting it get repetitive or predictable. (Look at the recipe section for some easy ideas suitable for every day.)

• Make sure that any fruit you serve is fully ripe, or it will be hard, unsweet, tasteless, and less digestible. Also, unripe fruit can cause stomach-ache and put children off wanting it again.

However, unripe fruit travels better and often looks better on display, so fruit on sale in shops is often not ready to eat. Ignore the use-by date and use your own judgement – bananas, for example, can still be green on their display-until date! They are actually not ready until their skins are well-mottled with black. Grapes are usually not fully sweet until they begin to  soften slightly; kiwi fruit can often keep for weeks and get juicier and sweeter; pears are almost always sold rock hard and can take two or three weeks to soften; plums, peaches and nectarines usually need several days to sweeten up; red and white currants are often picked under-ripe and need a day or two in the sun to become nice.

So except for soft red fruits which deteriorate rapidly, be prepared to buy fruit well in advance.

• To store fruit: keep citrus fruits cold, even refrigerated, to make them taste special. Most soft summer fruits need refrigerating as do apples if they are to stay crisp. Other fruits need air and warmth. Never put bananas in the fridge or they will spoil.

• As soon as fruit is cut it begins to lose flavour and vitamin C, although if it is chilled these losses will be smaller. So keep vitamin C-rich citrus fruits and kiwi fruits cold and cut them up at the last moment.

> " Every Friday night I make a fruit platter of bite-sized pieces of fruit and the children dig in with cake forks while they watch television."

• Without making heavy weather of it, just assume that your family will eat fruit on and off through the day. Put some out at every meal and also have some around the home for anyone to 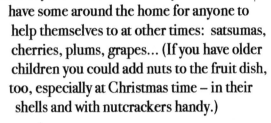 help themselves to at other times: satsumas, cherries, plums, grapes... (If you have older children you could add nuts to the fruit dish, too, especially at Christmas time – in their shells and with nutcrackers handy.)

• If you buy fruits that are in season, you will automatically have variety through the year. The first cherries arrive in June, followed by nectarines, peaches, apricots, strawberries, raspberries, red, white and black currants and watermelons. Blackberries, Victoria plums, figs, greengages and damsons mark the end of the soft fruit season. English apples are mostly harvested between August and October. Make a point of buying lots of these delicious fruits while they are around.

> "To make some variety, I purposely stop buying apples, all citrus fruit, bananas, pineapple, kiwi fruit and grapes in the summer because I can get these all the rest of the year, and we go mad on all the summer fruit. When I see the Switzen plums on the market I know that's the end of summer for another year. We celebrate autumn with apples off our tree, and then go back to all the things we stopped buying."

> " Hurrah for summer! It seems that children will eat endless amounts of red summer fruit!"

• Farmers' markets and other small-scale sales outlets can have unusual varieties. Their often intriguing names add to the pleasure.

• For bargain soft fruit, visit your local market late in the day – Saturday afternoon is a good time.

• Some people have fruit trees in their gardens but, unbelievably, 'can't be bothered' (!) or are too old or infirm to pick the fruit. If you know someone like this, consider tactfully offering to pick it for them, perhaps with your (well-behaved) children, and ask if you could buy some of it from them. An elderly or housebound person might be extremely pleased that their beautiful fruit is not all going to be wasted. Also, the apples may be of some unusual, old variety never on sale in shops, probably delicious – and 100% organic!

• Shop around for apples that actually taste good – some don't, and no more can we buy those delicious little Cox's that were around for years (the trees were old and uneconomical so they were grubbed up). Try different varieties and see which your children like best.

• Home grown apples may not always look supermarket-perfect (although many do) but shape has nothing to do with flavour. Some apples, especially from neglected trees, may have 'scab', an apple tree disease, but this doesn't affect people at all, so just cut off the dark spots on the peel. If codling moths have attacked an apple, you might find a tiny maggot in the centre, or if it has already crawled out, you might see its exit tunnel. Show this to your children (if it won't put them off) as something of interest. A mini biology lesson! The rest of the apple is perfectly good to eat.

• When picking fruit, you might find that the birds have been there first – if so, you will be able see the little pointed holes made by their beaks. Again, show your child. Say that the birds always go for the ripest fruits, and so when you've cut off the bit around the pecking-holes, the rest (well-washed) should be especially good.

• Go on an outing to a pick-your-own farm and enjoy sunshine and harvesting.

> "We always collect our daughter from pre-school with a yummy treat of fresh fruit, and it's *always* different, *always* a surprise and *always* chopped and peeled, ready to go. She loves it, and the other parents and children and staff have noticed, so we're starting a trend! She fills up just enough to be hungry again for tea at 5 p.m."

• Go blackberrying. If you live in a town, there may be hidden treasures in surprising places such as uncultivated parts of a cemetery or around the edges of sports fields. Let children eat as they go as well as picking some to bring home. (Take a damp cloth for wiping purple hands and faces, and dress in clothes that will take stains.) Teach them about picking only the fully ripe ones – the ones that pull easily off their stalks.

• Mash blackberries into plain yoghurt with the merest speck of sugar. A pinch of mixed spice cuts any tartness too. This dessert is worth it for the brilliant purple colour alone.

• Make your fruit desserts look terrific. Set them off on pretty serving dishes, or serve in glass bowls or goblets with small spoons. Think of the colours you are putting together In a fruit salad or other fruit arrangement, try to add something very dark – a few black grapes, blackberries, black currants, deep red or black cherries, for an eye-catching effect.

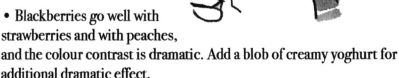

• Blackberries go well with strawberries and with peaches, and the colour contrast is dramatic. Add a blob of creamy yoghurt for additional dramatic effect.

• Black currants have hugely more vitamin C than any other fruit. They can be a bit tart, but only a few are needed for colour contrast in fruit dishes. Freeze some for winter for their useful colour.

> "I always serve cold desserts in tall sundae glasses, and we eat with long-handled spoons – café style! It makes the fruit seem very special and my two girls love eating it like that. They think it's the normal way to eat dessert."

• Create a 'fruit treat'. Find something you don't often have – perhaps an 'extra-sweet' little pineapple, the first English strawberries of the summer, the first Victoria plums (what a short season they have!), a box of sweet white currants, a guava, an ugli fruit, a whole watermelon, red grapefruit, a bag of huge black cherries... Make a big thing of it, especially with young children, so they think it's something special too.

• On a hot summer's day, buy some watermelon and let children (or all of you) eat it outdoors in huge slices, spitting out the pips (if they're swallowed it doesn't matter) and slurping the juice. Messy garden or picnic fun.

• Make fruit 'lollipops' by freezing:

  - halved, peeled bananas

  - orange segments

  - nectarine slices

  - strawberries

  - thin slices of watermelon – monster-pops!

Could the children think of appropriate names for each kind? You can also make lollipops by pouring the following mixtures into small pots. If you push a wooden spatula into the centre of each pot when the mixture is half frozen it will stand upright. Amongst other ideas, try:

  - freshly squeezed orange juice, sometimes mixed with yoghurt

  - any puréed fruit, raw or cooked

  - puréed fruit mixed with yoghurt or a little cream

  - stewed, puréed fruit, sweetened with a little honey

  - puréed fruit and juice, such as strawberries and orange juice

Keep the flavours strong because some flavour is lost in freezing.

• Make ice-cream using the mixtures above. Strictly speaking, without cream (or yoghurt) they are sorbets, so call them that if you like. Add yoghurt or a little thick cream (not single, it's tasteless), and you have 'real' ice-cream. If you haven't got an ice-cream maker, stir the mixture once or twice while it's freezing to prevent ice crystals forming – or omit that stage: it's a fine point.

• You could use the above ideas for fruit mixtures as sauces to serve with fresh fruit. Strawberry-and-orange sauce is luscious over whole strawberries – and also over peaches, nectarines, blackberries, raspberries and chopped orange segments.

• Also use the above ideas as fruit sauces to serve in generous amounts with little home-made cakes, especially cakes still warm from the oven.

• If your children yearn for 'shop' ice-cream (they may not after tasting yours), you could at least serve it with your own fruit sauce. Otherwise, serve the ice-cream with plenty of fresh fruit pieces such as peaches, mango, plums, bananas, apricots or any summer red fruits. (Let a little shop ice-cream completely melt and see how some kinds just turn into foam!)

• Perhaps buy an ice-cream scoop to get 'proper' shaped ice-cream. Or use two spoons dipped in hot water to make professional looking, lozenge-shaped scoops. Or buy ice-cream cones. Or, of course, children can simply eat the ice-cream out of the pot it was made in.

> "After a 'food day' at school, they requested watermelon: they'd been painting one and said it looked so delicious. We had to make a special trip (*very* welcome) to get one!"

• Make a 'sweet pizza' with fruit purée instead of tomato sauce and lots of fruit pieces (which children can cut up) on top. Eat with yoghurt, smatana, fromage frais, evaporated milk or crème fraîche. It makes a good tea-time dish.

• Peach surprise: cut a peach in half, remove the stone and put in a raspberry or a little piece of marzipan, and reassemble the peach.

• When you make a cake (perhaps with a child helping), cut it open, spread with a little crème fraîche, fill with lots of chopped fruit moistened with orange juice and reassemble. Spread a little more crème fraîche on the top. Perhaps your child would like to carefully decorate it with various different-coloured fruits. (See the recipes on pages 179 and 180.)

"My son, aged four, will eat fruit if he prepares it."

"My daughter loves grilled fruit such as grilled apple rings."

"My little daughter made us a fruit salad with grapes, pear, banana and orange juice."

"My two boys will eat endless cherries if they can eat them in the garden and squirt the stones."

• Think of ways of making the same fruit look different. For example, when eating oranges, you could divide them into segments, or cut into quarters (nice and messy to eat), or very thin wedges, or into rounds or semi-circles. Sometimes arrange them in a pattern of overlapping pieces on a plate; sometimes put a 'twist' of orange in the centre, sometimes make a whole plateful of 'twists'. Perhaps your child could help with the slicing – closely supervised. If you know how, segment the orange professionally (i.e. remove all the membranes) for an exceptionally delicious experience.

Some of these ways are messy and will lose some juice, but don't worry about that – if the children are having fun and enjoying their orange-eating or orange-slicing experience it's well worth it. Let them remember what fun the oranges were.

• Squeeze an orange, or let children do it, for an exquisitely delicious drink, quite different from the 'freshly squeezed' orange juice on sale in supermarkets.

• Fizzy water and orange juice makes a good fizzy drink – children's Buck's Fizz! It's a good party drink, too.

• In January, make the most of blood oranges. Nowadays they are often called ruby oranges, but children will probably prefer the original name. At any rate, buy them often while they are around and enjoy their different-tasting, red-splashed flesh.

• As a cold weather treat, sauté pieces of fruit over high heat in very little butter-and-oil (or organic 'spreadable' butter) and a sprinkling of caster sugar. Serve at once, hot and caramelised around the edges. Try orange, pineapple and apple slices and whole bananas. Sometimes cook just one kind of fruit, sometimes a medley.

• In cold weather, serve hot fruity puddings, perhaps as a weekend treat: fruit crumbles, pies and tarts, apple pan dowdy, apple-and-blackberry pie...These take a little time to make but what pleasure they give! It's almost impossible of course to buy real puddings. Serve with cream-and-yoghurt or real custard or evaporated milk (see pages 177 and 184).

• Roast hunks of fruit in a hot oven or grill them. Optionally, sieve a very little caster sugar over them beforehand to caramelise slightly and make them utterly mouth-watering.

• Fill pancakes with raw or lightly grilled fruit and dust lightly with icing sugar.

> "The trick is to make fruit seem special and desirable. So instead of 'pushing' it and saying how healthy it is all the time, turn the situation on its head and say things like 'I've only just bought those grapes and they're nearly gone!' or 'I see the fruit bowl burglars have been again,' or 'Don't just gobble up those peaches, they're special.' It works!"

"When we go shopping, I ask each child to choose one kind of fruit. As they each choose something different we have some variety. Sometimes they choose quite exotic things or something unknown just to try it."

"When we go shopping, I ask my little girl to choose three different kinds of fruit, each one a different colour. It takes longer but it's worth it."

• For a cold day treat, apple fritters are unbelievably good. A nice idea for when your child has a friend (or friends) visiting.

• Bake little sponge cup cakes but cut the sugar by half and mix in lots of fresh fruit – blueberries, strawberries, stoned cherries, chopped nectarine or plum, and give them to your children – and any visiting friends – while the cakes are still warm. Irresistible.

• Spear hunks of pineapple, pear, peach or orange segments on lollipop sticks or, for older children, cocktail sticks.

• Fruit kebabs: you could thread pieces onto lollipop sticks, or, for older children, onto kebab sticks. Perhaps have a fruity dip, too: make a simple fruit purée or mix the purée with yoghurt or cream.

• Grill pieces of fruit on metal skewers for older children to slide off and eat while still warm.

• Don't just buy satsumas, try clementines which can be sweeter, and other similar fruits that appear from time to time. See which your children prefer.

• If you have a juicer or a high-speed liquidizer, older children could experiment with making smoothies from various fruits, supervised as necessary. They could also add bought fruit juice or yoghurt. With younger children, make smoothies together (and see page 173).

• To get fruit eaten, try serving a small amount of chocolate sauce with all kinds of fruity things, but be careful it never seems like a trap – that the chocolate is there only to get the fruit eaten. (See page 183.)

• Dip the tips of strawberries or orange segments in melted chocolate and arrange on a plate as a treat.

• Make a quick zigzag of chocolate sauce over the bowl of fruit salad or the fruit jelly, or make a spiral or a 'scribble'; or put one little blob in each person's bowl – or at least the child's bowl. Let a child have a go at it. One parent said 'Chocolate will get *any* fruit eaten!'

• Slivers of crystallised ginger can pep up a fruit dish enormously. A few slivers plus a little of their syrup can turn melon into an event! Curiously, a few grains of salt work wonders on melon too.

• Sometimes glaze the fruit with melted redcurrant jelly or sieved, melted apricot jam. It makes it look extremely special. Perhaps bake little tartlet cases, fill with small or chopped fruits and then glaze. Excellent for a party.

• Mash/chop soft fruits into yoghurt for a variety of desserts.

- Marble some puréed fresh or cooked fruit with custard and cream to make fruit fools.

- Serve fruit salads and puddings with evaporated milk: it's only milk that has been evaporated and so is a useful source of calcium. Unlike custard and ice-cream it's not sugared, and it's not fatty like cream. It's also cheap, easily stored in a cupboard and goes with almost everything.

- Also look for 'smatana', on sale in some delicatessens and supermarkets. It's also a milk product (a sort of cross between yoghurt and sour cream), unsweetened, much less fatty than cream, cheap, keeps well in the fridge and goes with almost everything. It's an eastern European food, not well known here but well worth searching for.

- Buy a strong, metal cherry stoner and give a child the job of firing cherry stones out of it – hopefully into a bowl. If they finish up eating a lot of the cherries, well ...fine!

- Make fruit jelly for dessert: make the jelly with orange juice and gelatine, and before it starts to set, pack it with sliced, soft fruits (see page 178). Don't use fresh pineapple as an enzyme in the raw fruit will prevent the jelly setting, but you could use tinned pineapple. Either let it set in a serving bowl, or individual glasses, or in an oiled mould such as a bread tin, and turn it out just before serving. For small children, make it in a traditional jelly mould. Eat as it is or with creamy yoghurt, smatana or ice-cream. A good party dish.

• As above, but arrange the fruit in distinct layers in a serving bowl or in individual glasses. Very attractive and party-ish. Perhaps top with ice-cream and/or chocolate sauce, or little blobs of smatana or whipped cream.

• Use little paper umbrellas to decorate fruity desserts in individual glasses, each one a different colour.

• Give your child an apple to polish! Wash it first, dry it, then let them rub it hard to give it a good shine – and make it 'theirs'. Could they polish an arrangement of apples for the dinner table?

"At a farmers' market stall which had a huge variety of dried fruits and nuts, my daughter and her friend picked bags of dried strawberries, kiwi fruit, apples, mango and raisins and happily munched their way around the rest of the market, satisfied with their bag of sweet goodies."

• Sieve a little cocoa powder over the top of desserts just before serving to make them look more appealing and sophisticated. Or perhaps use 100's and 1,000's, either coloured or chocolate.

• Scooped-out orange halves make good containers for fruit salads or other fruity desserts.

• Put kiwi fruit in egg cups. Cut off the tops and eat them like boiled eggs with little spoons.

> "My daughter will eat the raisins that come in small bright boxes from the supermarket, but refuses them out of an ordinary bag. I now buy raisins in bulk and fill up the little boxes for her."

• Mashed ripe banana on bread and butter is an excellent tea-time food, and a good snack for any time. In summer, also try mashed raspberries or strawberries.

• If you find that the soft summer fruit you have bought is of indifferent flavour, then cook it. Simmer it with a small amount of water or fruit juice plus a little sugar or honey. Depending on the proportion of sugar and the fruit itself, you will get either stewed fruit, fruit jelly or jam. In any case the fruit should now taste delicious.

• Adding a few drops of Crème de Cassis liqueur when you cook fruit gives a lovely rosy colour. Very attractive to children and adults alike.

• Never over-cook fruit or it will develop a slimy texture that children hate.

• Add currants, sultanas or raisins to fruit salads, green salads and rice salads, but make them juicy by simmering them in hot water for a few minutes. Or put them in a little cold water, bring to the boil, cover, turn out the heat, and let them sit for a couple of hours. They will plump up and become succulent. If you leave them until the next day, they will have almost turned back into grapes! (Once they have re-hydrated, they shouldn't be dried and stored again or they will rot.)

• Forget dates. Dates have the highest sugar content by far of any fruit and are also sticky, so the sugar sticks onto teeth much like sticky sweets.

• When buying dried apricots, go a bit easy on the yellow ones which have been treated with sulphur to preserve the colour. Go to a health shop for unsulphured ones which, unfortunately, are brown, but taste good and can be consumed at will.

• Adding chopped dried apricots to muesli enlivens it and gives it a bit of a tang.

> "When shopping for dried fruit in supermarkets – look out. It can be labelled as 'healthy', but we found that every item we'd bought had sugar added. Why?"
>
> "A friend gave us a pretty bowl filled with dried fruits and almonds, a lovely present – until we found that all the fruit and almonds were drenched in sugar which ruined them. At least the bowl was useful!"

• Bake banana bread. Perhaps eat it with cheese or more banana.

• Bake extra-fruity cakes and fruit loaves. Of course the recipes also call for sugar, but you can easily cut this down without anyone noticing, especially if you add extra dried fruit – just keep the total weight of fruit-plus-sugar the same. Serve the cake or loaf with strong Cheddar cheese, north country style. Cheese negates the acidic, enamel-destroying effect of sugar.

• If you think your children are eating too much acidic fruit (such as oranges) for the safety of their teeth, then serve both cheese and fruit at mealtimes, or get children to follow eating fruit with cheese – the tiniest piece will do. Cheese is alkali and neutralizes the acid in the fruit. Milk, also alkali, has a similar effect.

• The Italian way of ending a meal with ripe pears and Parmesan is an utterly scrumptious one. Shave thin curls off a hunk of Parmesan, and serve with pear slices. Nothing else is required. You can use a vegetable peeler or a special 'cheese plane'. Older children can shave their own pieces at the table along with the adults. The pears should be really ripe and juicy. Worth trying.

• Similarly, finish a meal with apple slices and strong Cheddar cheese.

• Go Continental: finish dinner with a cheese board *and* a fruit platter. Everyone dips in and takes a-bit-of-this and a-bit-of-that.

> "My children love the fruit display in our local supermarket and love helping themselves to things to eat".

> "As a treat when we go to the supermarket, I let my
> daughter fill a box for her lunch from the fruit salads bar.
> She loves doing it – though it can work out a bit expensive!"

• Pack plenty of fruity things when you go out for a picnic. Some
supermarkets now sell fruit snacks in small packets for picnics, but check
the prices – it might be cheaper to make your own mixture.

What's 'a portion' of fruit – or vegetable?

Answer. A handful, near enough. A child's handful for a
child, an adult's handful for an adult – your portion grows as
you do! Halve the amount for dried fruit.

For adults a medium-sized apple, banana or corncob, and
150ml of juice is about right. Under-fives need roughly half
these amounts.

One parent said "My daughter enjoys counting her portions
each day – and she checks me out too!"

• When you go out, keep something fruity (dried fruit, perhaps a small
apple) with you: if hunger strikes mid-trip, you have an instant healthy
solution. Saves frayed tempers too.

• Actually, not all children like sweet things. One father told us "my
little girl doesn't like *anything* sweet – sweets, chocolate, anything. The
only fruit she will touch is a Granny Smith apple. Of course, her teeth are
absolutely perfect!"

71

HOW TO GET CHILDREN TO EAT FISH

I always knew when our neighbours were having fish: I could smell it cooking. That well-known, truly awful smell would pervade the air for about half an hour.

What is less well known is that fish only smells like that when it's being ruined – that is, when it's being cooked too long or too fast – or both. When it's cooked slowly, and *just* to the point of being done, it has no odour at all. Our neighbours' fish must have been cooked to a rag. I imagined the reaction of their three children when confronted with the stuff, perhaps being urged to eat it, and, eventually, joining the ranks of the many people who say they hate fish. This is a peculiarly British phenomenon: people in other countries are amazed at our dislike of it and our reluctance to offer children anything beyond fish fingers. Such a pity, when fish is so easy and so quick to cook, so easy to digest – and when it can be so delicious!

Also, of course, it is highly nutritious. We are often reminded that we should eat more of it – three times a week according to some advice, and especially 'oily' fish because of their beneficial 'omega-3' oils. Salmon, trout, mackerel, sardines, herring and pilchards come into this category, and they are called 'oily' because their oil is distributed throughout their flesh. With so–called 'white' fish, such as cod, plaice, whiting, haddock and halibut, all the oil is in the liver.

What can be done to get children to eat fish? Well, if it's cooked well, there really shouldn't be any problem. Just start them off on it in babyhood so they grow up with it as a familiar, enjoyable taste.

I had my first fish today!

• Offer babies over six months old individual flakes of white fish (whiting is the easiest to digest as well as being very economical) as finger food. At nine months, offer flakes of a mild oily fish such as salmon or trout.

• Keep fish on the menu. Cook different kinds of fish and have a range of recipes.

• Young children can be fascinated by fish shops so allow time to look at the fish. I recently watched a mother help her four year old to choose 'his' fish for his tea, which was then wrapped separately in 'his' parcel for him to carry!

• Eat fish together and with obvious pleasure. If you have any personal dislikes, beware of passing them on.

• Cook fish *slowly*. It must be only *just* done. Cook small strips of it gently for two to three minutes in a shallow pan containing just enough oil or water to prevent sticking. Otherwise, microwaving them on a lightly oiled plate, will take about ten seconds. Raw fish is slightly translucent; as soon as it's become opaque right through, it's cooked. Salmon turns pale pink when it's done.

• Fish soon spoils when it's kept warm, so get everything else ready first so you can serve it immediately it's done.

• Check fish meticulously for bones, even filleted fish (but ignore the tiny, floppy, hair-like ones in oily fish like sardines, trout and herring).

Never give a child a fright over a bone – it could put them off for life. Train children to check for bones as they eat, too. (You can mash the spine bones of tinned fish as they are soft and a superb source of calcium. Older children can enjoy fishing them out and crunching them!)

• Try to avoid presenting a child with what could seem like a huge slab of unadorned white stuff, and white fish on a white plate rarely looks appetising. Make it look attractive. Perhaps build it into composite dishes, or cover it with a tasty sauce or a crunchy topping of cheese and breadcrumbs. On the other hand, some children like to see what they are getting, in which case put the sauce and any 'toppings' at the side of the fish.

• For a young child, serve sardines or other small fish 'swimming' on a bed of shredded lettuce. You could add other maritime ideas, such as purple chive flowers (quite edible) to look like sea urchins! Perhaps decorate the plate further with well-washed sea shells ('fishes' homes'), or a halved potato as a desert island, or put the sardines on a rectangle of toast and say they are floating on the sea on a raft... Have fun thinking up other ideas with your child.

However, if your child seems to think of all this as something to play with rather than eat, then make it less fanciful. Also, if you make too much of decorating the fish, a child could become suspicious as to why you are making so much of it and be put off. As always, observe the child's reactions, and adjust accordingly.

• For a young child, cook a small piece of fillet of whiting (the mildest flavour) or haddock or plaice, put it on a coloured plate and surround with little vegetables: blobs of creamed spinach, a few thin beans sliced thinly and diagonally, tiny carrot sticks for colour and a few *petits pois*; plus a little buttery mashed potato. (What price a fish finger now!)

• For a young child, put a piece of crispy-coated herring fillet (see page 150) on a cushion of buttery mashed potato on a coloured plate. Decorate with parsley sprigs, curly lettuce leaves, chopped chives and a wedge of lemon for him to squirt.

• For a young child, put a small piece of crispy mackerel fillet on a cushion of mashed potato in the middle of a plate. Surround the potato with a golden sea of apricot sauce, filling the entire plate. (See recipe on page 148.)

• Bacon is wonderful with any kind of fish. Try frying slivers of bacon in a pan, and when they're done, adding slivers of fish. Sometimes cook chopped (fresh) tomatoes with the bacon. Similarly, wrap thin pieces of ham around fingers of fish. Bake with finely sliced onions or microwave.

• Some children like fish when it's pink, so stir tomato purée into tinned tuna to make a deeper colour. Serve trout or salmon (possibly tinned). Make pink fish-cakes with salmon or tuna and add a little tomato purée (see page 148). Little fish-cakes make good finger food

• Similarly, make pink mayonnaise by stirring in tomato purée, and serve with fish such as salmon or tuna.

• Pack the pink fish-cake mixture, or any fishcake mixture, into an oiled fish-shaped mould and turn it out onto a 'sea' of peas, green beans or shredded lettuce.

• Toss fingers of white fish in breadcrumbs or crushed whole-wheat cereals, and fry briefly in a speck of oil. The crunchy exterior is an attraction. Home-made fish fingers!

• For extra flavour, toss pieces of white fish in a mixture of breadcrumbs and a little grated Parmesan cheese – or any hard, tasty cheese. Fry in a speck of oil or in oil and bacon fat.

• To coat any pieces of white fish the professional way, toss in flour, then dip quickly in either beaten egg or milk, and then coat with fine breadcrumbs. Then fry. The coating will be crispy and delicious.

• Look out for 'gefilte fish' – delicious coated balls of minced fish.

• For an orangey-brown coating, pulverize some All-bran crumbs and use for coating fish cakes or home-made fish fingers for a change.

• Two tips for avoiding greasy fried fish dishes: 1) instead of oiling the pan, try painting or spraying a little oil directly on the food and 2) drain the cooked fish on absorbent paper

• To sweeten the somewhat dry taste of white fish, serve with a good tomato sauce or a good white sauce into which you've stirred plenty of pan-fried mushrooms, grated cheese or chopped fresh parsley (see pages 159 and 160).

• Serve sweet-tasting vegetables with white fish: tiny peas, French and runner beans, mushrooms or ratatouille (make a simple stew of tomatoes, peppers, courgettes, onions and aubergines). Save the cabbage family and carrots for meat and vegetarian dishes, although a carrot and potato purée goes well with fish.

• Make a little mashed-potato nest. Into it put some cooked fish and some sauce. Sprinkle with cheese and grill to lightly brown.

• If your child likes lentils, purée some red ones and make either a nest or a cushion for some fish.

• Make a nest by coiling round a long thin fillet of fish. Put mashed potato or a rice mixture such as rice, peas and sweet corn in the middle. Perhaps colour the rice with turmeric, or purée some carrot into the potato to give it colour.

• A scallop shell holds enough fish for a young child and looks pretty. Press it into a blob of play dough or raw pastry so it doesn't tip up.

> "The first time I ever ate crab was when I was at Brownies, and someone brought some crabs' claws and shared them out. We dug the meat out with our hair grips! Not very hygienic, but I remember thinking how good the crab tasted. I've liked it ever since, and now, many years later, I buy a crab every week all through the summer."

• Children can enjoy digging small shellfish out of their shells: try winkles, whelks, shrimps or lightly crushed crabs' claws. Good just for fun, or perhaps as a snack with bread and butter. If you find a seaside whelk stall, make use of it.

• The best tasting crabs are spider crabs. They're not common, but worth looking out for – ask your fishmonger to try and get one for you. Their meat is easier to get out of the body, too. Wonderful for a picking, cracking, gouging meal with jacket potato, salad and mayonnaise. Children might love the name but if you think they won't, use the American name: snow crab.

• On a serving plate, put out a 'fish medley': small chunks of any white fish, fresh or tinned salmon or tuna, 'ocean sticks', prawns, crab claws, shrimps, winkles, pieces of buckling, smoked eel. Add lemon slices and parsley sprigs. Good finger food. Vary the mixture from time to time.

• Paella is great-looking as well as great for hiding pieces of fish. Remember to add prawns, and have freshly cooked mussels in their shells on top for spectacular effect.

• Cook kedgeree, but as the traditional smoked fish is very salty, mix it half-and-half with white fish. Colour it yellow by frying turmeric for one minute with the onion (see page 150). Optionally, decorate with quartered hard-boiled eggs.

• Tinned fish, especially sardines, are particularly nutritious and a terrific source of calcium. Serve with a salad of baby tomatoes, radishes, avocado chunks and thin slices of cucumber, and with hunks of French bread to mop up the oily juices. This makes a good mid day or supper dish.

• Halve sardines, cut into long diagonals and scatter on pizzas. Older children might enjoy tiny pieces of anchovy too (soak them in milk for ten minutes to remove some of their salt). Try other tinned fish. Fish is traditional on pizza, if anyone asks!

• Use mashed tinned sardines, kipper or pilchards beaten into cream cheese or curd cheese as a sandwich or pitta filling; or pile it on a bap or a toasted muffin or triangles of bread. Decorate or surround with fingers of cucumber or salad greens, which may also get eaten.

• Make a quick paté with smoked mackerel, horseradish and cream cheese. The horseradish makes it zingy.

• Beat a little butter, lemon juice and seasoning into some tinned cod's roe, adding a drop of yoghurt to moisten. Pile on hot toast for a good snack or tea time dish with crispy lettuce and cucumber fingers.

• Serve halved or roughly chunked sardines on a bed of shredded lettuce on triangles of hot toast. Good as party food, too, for older children.

• For a party special, beat puréed smoked eel into cream cheese and serve on baps or on pieces of hot toast. Expensive but stunningly good.

• Appetite-enhancing decorations for fish dishes include warmed potato crisps, prawns, pan-browned mushroom slices, bacon bits, olives, croutons, dabs of tarragon- or parsley-butter, grapes, toasted breadcrumbs, lemon wedges ... and cream.

• And don't forget kippers! Undyed ones are nicest and are less salty. Grill lightly (see page 149). Good for winter tea-times and weekend breakfast with toast.

Go fishing!

This could be part of a seaside camping holiday, in which case the fish can be eaten immediately and be extra delicious. Fried in butter over an open fire, it is wonderful. Otherwise keep it chilled and take it home to eat the same day.

• Exclaim over pictures of extraordinary-looking tropical fish. Could your child paint a picture of an imaginary, fantastic-looking fish?

• Drool over pictures of fish dishes in cookery books and magazines.

• Children can be fascinated by the different kinds of fish and shellfish in the fishmonger's and supermarket. One mother said 'My son loves looking in the fishmonger's window - we always have to go that way home from school!'

• Let your child hold a whole unwashed fish and feel how slippery it is (herrings are small and cheap but trout are one of the slipperiest). You could discuss what makes fish so slippery; and then scrub off the scales and see if it's as slippery as before. Put it in a tray of water and observe it more closely. Why are fishes' eyes so big but with no eyelids? What are the fins for? Why are so many fish a blueish colour?

• At the seaside, collect sea shells. What creature lived in this shell and that one?

• Go fishing with magnets-on-'fishing-rods' and cardboard fish with paper clips on them. Sing '1, 2, 3, 4, 5, Once I caught a fish alive'.

HOW TO GET CHILDREN TO EAT BREAKFAST

'Breakfast gets the day's work done', wrote nutritionist Adelle Davies, many years ago, and it's a still a good motto. And it's easy to prove. If you don't normally eat any breakfast (a quarter of the British workforce are reputed to go to work on nothing but a cup of tea), or if you just snatch a slice of toast or bowl of cereal, try the following and notice the difference. Each morning have sliced cheese, or a poached or scrambled egg on wholewheat toast, plus a glass of milk (or hot *café crème* – see page 87). It is almost guaranteed that you will have more energy throughout the day until mid-to-late afternoon. You almost cetainly won't be 'falling through the earth' by mid morning or needing the pick-up of a chocolate bar. (Of course there are other good breakfasts but this one is quick to eat.)

Once the value of a good breakfast is realized, and breakfast becomes a part of the day's routine, much of the problem of getting children to eat it can just disappear.

In term-time, of course, having a good breakfast is especially crucial. Most children will have a journey to school, perhaps a long one, and nowadays it cannot be assumed there will be any food worth eating at school. In any case, even a large mid-day meal does not compensate for a poor breakfast: the morning is already lost and a big midday meal can lead to drowsiness in the afternoon.

Another bonus is that children are likely to be calmer and better-behaved after eating a good breakfast. Without a good breakfast, they could be hungry by mid morning or even before school begins – after all, they will have been virtually fasting since the previous day. Their blood levels will be low, leading to feelings of tiredness and/or crossness, so children with access to sugary snacks may be only too glad to grab them to give themselves a much-needed energy boost.

Of course, the sugary snack produces its own problems: some children can become quite 'high' after eating even a moderate amount of sugar, which can cause them to behave badly, thus producing further problems. With some children there can be a daily pattern of sugar-snacking, with high and low blood sugar levels corresponding with highs and lows of energy and mood. Fizzy drinks are major culprits.

What's a suitable breakfast for children?

It might seem that children's breakfast cereals are the answer. Certainly, the packets look terrific: imaginative, child-centred, sometimes funny, with 'free gifts', cut-outs and things to collect . . . they can be almost irresistible to children. However, most cereals are from about a third to nearly *half* pure sugar! Some are also very salty. All seem to be made from refined, i.e. not wholegrain, cereal (and see chapter 7 on shopping with children).

KIDZ KRUMMY KRUNCH

80% MORE SUGAR FREE

Also, these cereals are so light that although it might look like quite a big helping as you pour it into the bowl, there isn't actually very much food there. Here's a little activity for the breakfast-provider:

Into a bowl, pour the amount of cereal you normally would for your child. Tip it out and crush it to a powder with a rolling pin. Will it fill an egg cup? Look at it and ask yourself if that seems enough for a growing child's first meal of the day. Oh, and remember, anything from about thirty to forty-odd percent of it is sugar, so remove that amount of powder and have another look. (And *what* did it cost?)

So the first tip is to completely avoid 'children's' breakfast cereals (and also most adult ones which can be much the same but with different pictures) and provide a *meal* instead. Make sure there's a good protein food in the meal, as that's what will see children through the day.

Breakfast ideas

- Whole wheat toast with:

 - a poached or scrambled egg

 - cheese, either cold or grilled lightly (cooked cheese is harder to digest)

 - hummus, with a smear of honey

 - sliced tomatoes mixed with grated cheese, lightly grilled

 - herring roes (fry in a speck of butter; a few seconds only) with chopped parsley and lemon juice

 - sardines and lemon juice

- an omelette, perhaps with chives, tomato, cheese or ham, and whole wheat toast (use organic 'spreadable' butter for spreading and cooking)

- 'second chance' omelette: any leftover meat, fish, vegetables or fruit from the previous evening could be put into an omelette if the recipient would enjoy it. You could even plan for this. Ratatouille omelette is terrific, for example. You are limited only by your family's palate.

 - a sweet omelette filled with banana, nectarine, plum, blackberries or strawberries; plus toast.

- pieces of undyed kipper (grilled for 7 minutes, skin side down (see page 149) with toast.

- 'eggy-bread': fingers or triangles of whole wheat bread dipped in beaten egg and quickly fried. Call it French toast or golden bread if you think that will go down better.

- a low-sugar cereal (such as crumbled Weetabix, Shredded Wheat, Puffed Wheat, or a mixture, with plenty of milk, but also something else such as toast or bread fingers with cheese, egg or ham.

> "My family always operated a sort of 'do-it-yourself' Muesli bar. My father would buy all different kinds of nuts and seeds and wheat flakes and oat flakes, as well as all kinds of dried fruits and each one was put into its own jar in our big larder. At breakfast, the jars would be put on the table and we would make up our own 'muesli' mixture and experiment – the jars weren't always the same. It was years before I realized you could buy muesli ready made!"

Home-made 'muesli': porridge oats mixed with crumbled whole wheat cereals, sultanas, chopped dried (unsulphured) apricots and other dried fruits, and chopped fresh fruit (apple-and-banana, strawberry-and-peach, banana-and-grape, and so on). Prepare the mixture in advance, perhaps in bulk, adding the fresh fruit at breakfast time. Eat with milk and plain, creamy yoghurt. For older children, you can add seeds (sunflower, sesame, pumpkin, linseed) and nuts, perhaps chopped – Brazil nuts can be a good choice because of their plentiful selenium. Whole hazelnuts and almonds can look inviting (and see page 172).

- for older children, a bought, unsugared muesli, although it needs 'chewing time'. Most bought 'mueslis' have sugar added and may bear little resemblance to the original muesli idea. Your supermarket will probably have just one unsweetened one – its own brand, with an all-fruit version and a nut-and-fruit version (nuts pieces can easily be inhaled by young children and are not recommended for under fives). These mueslis vary a bit from brand to brand, so make comparisons if you can. They often go on special offer twice a year in January and August, but you can make them more economical by mixing in some rolled oats. Sliced dried apricots give a tang and prevent blandness. Extra nuts and seeds as above add texture, crunch and superb nutritive value. Add fresh fruit as above.

- home-made granola. Commercial ones can be extremely high in sugar and toasted hard, but you can avoid this when you make your own, and it still tastes wonderful (see recipe on page 172). In fact, it tastes so good that even hard-line breakfast avoiders can get seduced by it.

- porridge or Readybrek made with all milk; instead of sugar, add a half teaspoon of honey, sultanas and thinly sliced banana. Adding a can of (unsweetened) evaporated milk will give it an extra creamy taste. If it's made the day before it will be even nicer!

And to drink?

Fruit juice (real, unsweetened) will help to release the iron in such foods as eggs and dried fruit.

Milk is excellent, but best towards the end of the meal in case it curtails appetite. Cold milk could be flavoured with vanilla and nutmeg or turned into a very nutritious shake (see page 174). Otherwise, it can appear as 'hot *café crème*'. Heat a cupful of milk so it's *just* hot enough to drink – not hotter or the taste will be spoiled. Stir in a few coffee granules. This is actually a delicious drink for anyone and can be useful at bedtime as, unlike most 'bed-time' drinks, it doesn't come with sugar added.

Tips:

• If your morning routine always involves breakfast then eating it becomes just a normal part of the day and not an issue.

• Aim to make it enjoyable with good food and a good atmosphere.

• Help your children to be hungry for breakfast by making sure their evening meal is not too late. Otherwise they could still be digesting yesterday's food when they get up the following morning and not feel hungry until after they've left for school. For the same reason, beware of serving a very heavy meal in the evening.

• Variety helps with some children. Sometimes have toast, sometimes warm some rolls; vary the way you cook the eggs, the fillings in the omelettes, and the ingredients in your muesli – unless your family likes predictability.

• Be flexible! Why not pizza, cheesy jacket potato or cold chicken if it's available and if that's what the child really wants? Adult rules about which food is suitable for which meal have little meaning for young children, and, nutritionally, are neither here nor there. If your child suggests a wholesome food for breakfast, cheer! Serve it if you can, whatever it is.

• In sunny summer weather, consider having breakfast out of doors as a treat. Much more may be eaten – but allow extra time.

> "I'm always puzzled to hear someone say they 'can't eat breakfast', because when I stay in a B&B, where breakfast is included in the price, everyone seems to come down and eat absolutely everything they're offered!

• Some families enjoy a leisurely family breakfast at the weekend, often with weekend 'specials': warmed croissants, home-made marmalade, muffins, bacon and eggs, banana bread, or a cheese board, for example.

I knew of one family whose Sunday breakfast was virtually brunch. It was a nice family occasion during which the father read a chapter of a book – his weekly 'serial' – to his two young children and their mother.

> "My son would often say he didn't want any breakfast, but I'd open the kitchen door wide and start cooking the bacon or kippers very slowly, so the smell would waft upstairs for a while. He'd be down pretty soon, and he'd eat a good breakfast."

> "My teenage boys would *not* get up in time to eat any breakfast. I nagged and nagged, until in the end I just took the breakfast upstairs to them and let them eat it in bed. They did actually manage to sit up and eat. My own mother was appalled! Well I didn't like it either, but I was desperate, and at least I knew they had gone to school every day with a good breakfast inside them."

> "When I went to secondary school, I had a longer journey and could never get up (or even wake up) in time to eat breakfast. My mother would stand in front of the front door, barring my way with a cup of hot milk in her hand, which I would gulp down before she'd let me through the door. That was my breakfast! But at least my poor mother had made sure that I'd had *something*."

• Try to eat breakfast with your children if you can. If you all leave the house at different times and get up accordingly, perhaps eat sometimes with one child, sometimes with another.

• Getting things ready the night before as much as possible can avoid much early morning rush. Of course getting up early enough – and going to bed at a good hour – helps too.

• If you never seem to manage to eat together in the evening, then consider making breakfast the family meal of the day. I knew of at least one family who actually ate their *dinner* at breakfast time! A very unusual arrangement of course (although, not, I'm told, unique), but this family liked it.

'Otherwise,' they said, 'We would hardly ever have seen each other. And yes, our breakfast was a proper dinner – steak and kidney pie and the lot, all got ready the evening before obviously and left to slow-cook overnight. If we hadn't had dinner in the morning we'd never have had it. I remember going off to school feeling ready for anything. I don't think we got really hungry again until the evening!"

• If all else fails, then serve a liquid breakfast (see page 174).

The sugar fix

"I remember teaching one particular, badly behaved little boy. It was strange, because he seemed quite nice in a way, but he was perpetually 'on the go'. He flicked crayons at other children and pushed their books onto the floor; he would fall off his chair and pretend he couldn't get up; he kept giggling helplessly over nothing; he dropped things on purpose... even at story time he wriggled and fidgeted.

At my wits' end, I asked his mother to come and see me. I asked her a question that I have often found useful. I said 'Does he have a really good breakfast in the morning?'

She replied 'Well, in a way, but he really only likes sugar. He pours it on everything. I have to hide the sugar bowl or he'll empty it. He looks for packets of biscuits and eats the lot. The doctor says he shouldn't eat so much sugar.'

I told her about the effect of sugar on behaviour, and persuaded her to allow him *none*. The result? After three days he was a completely different child. End of problem!

However, after several weeks, he began to slip back, so I spoke to his mother again. 'Oh, I forgot!' she exclaimed. 'He's been having sugar again!' She stopped it a second time and again, after three days, he was behaving completely differently. It does make me wonder how much sugar other badly-behaved and problematic children are eating for breakfast – and at other times – every day.

HOW TO SURVIVE SHOPPING WITH CHILDREN

We all know the scene – a mother and child are arguing in the supermarket over some food or other. The mother is insisting that her view will prevail and the child is also insisting, hoping to change her mother's mind. Eventually one or the other will win. If the child wins, peace will reign – until next time, but the mother can be left feeling angry, perhaps guilty at giving in and possibly embarrassed by the public battle. Even if the mother wins, she may still be left feeling angry and embarrassed – and perhaps guilty for disappointing her child. Whoever wins, there's no happy ending.

But why are such scenes so common? Why should a child be so desperate for a particular breakfast cereal or a certain brand of yoghurt or soft drink? The answer, of course, is that it's a set-up: it's 'pester power', the manufacturers' pot of gold.

Just one look at the child-centred design of the brightly coloured packets and tubs reveals all: the food-packaging is turned into a plaything, and may bear no relation to its contents at all. As well as pictures of funny faces and cartoon, film or story-book characters, there can be 'free gifts', pictures to cut out and play with, a whole series of things to save ('seven to collect!'), even perhaps a direct message to the child ('You'd be a LOONY to miss out!'). Further, many children will already be familiar with the pictures on the packaging from the multitude of advertisements that pepper their TV programmes. We can hardly blame children for being seduced.

Young problems

"Young children can't read. They just see the picture and they want the packet."

"Character branding of foods makes them so seductive – even to an 18-month old. It's frightening."

"My three insist on certain branded items when they know they don't like them. They've come to believe these products must be good, and it's they (or their memory) that must be at fault."

"It's easy for an adult to underestimate the power of advertising – until you become a parent."

In a way, the packages are brilliant, and if they contained something other than what they do we might applaud them. Unfortunately, one major disadvantage of 'children's foods' is that they are more than likely to be stuffed with sugar – for example, the amount in nearly all 'children's' cereals ranges from a third to nearly *half*. Cereals – and other foods – can also be high in salt, which inhibits the absorption of calcium. In fact three quarters of foods sold as suitable for children are stuffed with sugar and/or artificial

EVERY BODY LOVES SUGAR AND FAT!

sweeteners, hydrogenated (saturated) fat or salt – or all three. Their very sweet, very salty or succulently fatty taste is all part of the enticing package. They require almost no chewing, although they may pleasantly crackle in the mouth before turning to pap.

In addition, they may also contain an array of additives, some of which can adversely affect behaviour. For years, The Hyperactive Children's Support Group have said that they could 'cure' eight of every ten children referred to them, simply by removing certain foods from the child's diet.

Now, government-sponsored research has found that certain additives do indeed produce hyperactive behaviour. The additives studied in this research are four colourings and one preservative:

E102 (tartrazine)
E110 (sunset yellow)
E122 (carmoisine)
E124 (ponceau)
E211 (sodium benzoate preservative)

The report also said that avoiding these additives would benefit *all* children. Therefore, it would seem wise for parents to check every label for (at least) these particular additives. (Also see pages 140 and 141.)

Parents can also be targeted: A 'flash' on the product declares it has added calcium, or some vitamin or other. But the amounts of added nutrients are very small, usually the smallest the manufacturer can put in and legally make the claim. Of course, nowhere does it list all the nutrients that were lost in processing the food. One nutritionist said 'It's like someone taking a fiver out of your purse and then boasting that they've put in a penny.' Nevertheless, feeding off parental anxieties, the ploy can be a very effective sales technique.

How can parents deal with this onslaught?

It's difficult. But the first tip is to realize what is going on, what the agenda is, and that thousands – perhaps millions – of other parents are in the same boat, and possibly just as angry. Remember, always, YOU, not the child, are in charge of what you buy.

Tips:

• Plan the week's menus – every meal and every snack, every drink. Go for health, variety and fabulous flavours. Write it all down and post it up. One parent said "In the holidays my children write the weekly menus and stick them on the fridge. It makes life easier and reduces complaints. It's amazing what they choose – chicken salad with Caesar dressing; white fish and mashed potato!"

• Go for 'ingredients' for home cooking, rather than ready-made foods, so the question of additives and added sugars and salt hardly arises. (If you do want to buy a 'ready-made', scrutinize the label in the shop and then decide whether this is really what you want your child to swallow.)

AS SEEN ON PESTERVISION!

• Next, make your shopping list. Include every item you'll need to buy. Remember to check your fridge and cupboards. The more you need to budget, the more this detailed planning is a good idea.

• Then buy *only what's on the list* – unless you have a genuinely better idea. Having made most of your decisions at home, you can whizz round the supermarket! Much less time for a child to become bored or distracted by packaging.

• If your child asks for something you don't wish to buy, you can truthfully say 'It's not on the list this week'. You could always add 'Perhaps next week'.

• Talk to your children about marketing ploys. Tell them what people who make things do to make people want to buy them. Perhaps make it a game in which you are outwitting an enemy. Adopt a conspiratorial tone of voice and say 'Yes, the packet looks fun but let's find the label and see what they've put in.' And then exclaim 'Goodness, this is all toothache stuff! We don't want that do we?' or 'This isn't real strawberry, just red dye. How mean of them!' And then 'They hope people won't read the label so they'll buy the stuff'.

As well as being a good way for rejecting undesirable products, it is also excellent consumer education. If your child thinks he's lucky to have such a knowledgeable parent – he's right. Not all children get this kind of education.

> "Food companies keep people poor. For example, there's a certain wrapped chocolate biscuit that costs nearly 50p. That's almost half of a pound gone, yet there's hardly any food in it at all. I used to work in the food industry and I know that biscuit would have cost only a few pence to make. That's why I say food companies keep people poor."

• Make rejecting things fun. Feel free to exclaim 'Ugh!', 'Yuk!', 'Not on your life!', etc., as you pass them on the shelf, with your child joining in, or even doing it all for you. How enjoyable for a child to be able to criticize the adult world so freely! It may even give other shoppers pause for thought, too.

• Refuse to get involved in an argument in the shop. Just say something like 'We talked about this at home, remember? Those yoghurts are full of sugar, so it would be really silly to buy them', and then go to the next thing on your list. If pestering occurs, say 'I said No', and repeat it as often as necessary. Sound bored and avoid eye-contact. If you keep to the same strategy every time, the message will get through. Your child can't actually *make* you buy anything: you have to *decide* to buy it.

• Don't worry about having to be so firm. Sometimes parenthood is like that. You don't need to get your child's approval for what you do. Children can be adept at inducing parental guilt, but it's not in their long term interest for them to know they can twist you round their little finger any more than it's in yours. It isn't just a matter of food – it's your relationship, and what expectations you are giving them about life in general.

Success stories

"Shopping for fresh produce and or ingredients for home baking teaches children that processed food is unnecessary".

"My children know all about food and what's good for them because I talk to them about it. I explain why I'm buying this and not that. Now they tell me what we should buy!"

"If my son wants something off the shelf, I say 'Read the ingredients to me'. If he can't (because the words are too unknown) we don't get it."

"My three children read the contents and openly discuss them. If there are too many, and especially if any words don't sound like food, they reject the food and try to find something else."

"My two (8 and 10) read the labels and are frequently disgusted".

" My seven year-old said to my five year-old 'No you can't have Sunny Delight – it's rubbish!"

• Shop early in the day when shops are less busy. One parent said "I found the difference in time between shopping on a Wednesday morning and shopping on a Friday morning was enormous. Now I always manage to avoid the crowds and the long queues."

Just say no

"When we're shopping and my child says she wants something I don't want her to have, then I just say no and she knows that's the end of it."

Just say yes

"Being told 'no' is a hard thing for a young child to bear, and it leads to confrontation and tears, so say 'yes' instead – or 'yes, perhaps' anyway. I learned this from my mother who had a big family. It's the best way with little children.

"When a child asks for something you don't want her to have, say 'Yes, one day we'll get one of those', or 'Yes, perhaps one week we'll try that'. If necessary, explain you don't have enough money for it *this* week, or you'll *just* use up what you've got in the cupboard first, and so on. But the child has heard the word 'yes' and is satisfied. The subject is dropped and may never be mentioned again. If it is, you can give the same answer. Young children change their minds so quickly and so often that you don't really need to treat every request seriously. To keep saying 'no, no, no,' is asking for trouble. You must keep things pleasant.

"Of course, I suppose that if a child rumbled you, you'd have to give a proper answer, but I don't remember that ever happening – perhaps mine rumbled me but thought they hadn't a hope! Of course, when they're older you have to explain things a bit more, but even then it can still work."

Chicken's bottoms

"I put my two girls off chicken nuggets straightaway. I said 'You wouldn't want those – they're made from chickens' bottoms and chickens' faces'. They never asked for them again!"

"I used to work in a factory that made chicken nuggets and novelty foods like that. I'd never want to eat them. They don't put in what I'd call proper meat, only odds and ends."

• If you want to, involve children in some of the planning, but keep choices straightforward. Avoid saying something like 'Would you like to have chicken tonight?' (how can they know what they'll feel like having, hours later?) or 'But will you eat it?' (are they likely to say 'no'?). Anyway, you've planned the week's menus, haven't you, so you know exactly what you'll be having. Instead, ask about something specific:

'Which fruit shall we get for dinner tonight? We need two kinds.' If he can't decide, then you decide. If your child then says 'Oh, I wanted something else!' he's too late. Next time he'll know he must choose when asked or he'll lose his chance. It's teaching him about playing fair, keeping one's word and consideration for others all in one.

• Don't even walk down the aisles with the soft and fizzy drinks, the biscuits, the sweets, the crisps.... Approach the cereals from the opposite end from where the children's cereals are and return the same way.

• If you can, avoid using the baby seats in supermarket trolleys – they're generally tilted at exactly the right angle for babies to look up at the bright lights in the ceiling. Now wonder they cry!

> "When I enter the supermarket, I put my young daughter in the trolley seat and put a bag of seedless grapes next to her. We both pick at them and chat as we go round. It occupies her as well as giving her something to eat."

• Get a young child to choose a toy to take with them to play with when you shop, preferably something that can be clipped on a belt or slung over the shoulder.

• Try not to shop when you're tired – it will all seem even worse...

And if they get hungry while you're out?

• Have a meal before you set out. If you shop when either you or your child is hungry you are more likely to be tempted.

• Have some 'good' food with you, just in case. Take a bottle of plain water in case of thirst, especially in summer.

• Buy something to eat as soon as you enter the supermarket – fresh fruit, raisins and dried apricots have often saved the day! Let your child have as much choice as you can *in that section* only.

Keeping them amused

"I ask my child to help pick things out for me. I say things like 'Find the mushrooms with the longest stalks (because stalks are tastier)', or 'We need six big carrots all about the same size', and she enjoys it. And I always encourage her to look at food in shops – the fishmonger's is great."

"My daughter helps to fetch things when she knows where they are. If the supermarket's moved something we curse them together in a very woman to woman way!"

"Sometimes I pretend I can't see something and ask my two if they can. Then they enjoy showing me how clever they are!"

"I ask my three year-old to choose the fruit and vegetables. I say 'One of each colour'. It takes longer but she enjoys it."

"Just avoid supermarkets and use small shops where people know you and your children. An Italian delicatessen gave my children cheese and meat samples when the children expressed an interest."

"Play games like 'I spy' while you are queuing; also, take a magazine and point out (hopefully!) interesting pictures to talk about."

Staying out of it

"We shop online, so everything's delivered – easily the best solution. No pestering, no hassle. When we do go shopping it's usually to small local shops and it's quickly done and enjoyable, rather than a chore."

But the packet is wonderful!

• If your child is amused by imaginative and eye-catching packages, feel free to share your child's delight just as you would with other experiences. *Buying* the product, however, is something else entirely. Read the label and then explain simply that only the picture is nice, and say briefly what's wrong with the contents: 'Too much sugar,' etc.

• You could always buy it and throw the contents away. Thus the child has the desired packet and you have protected vulnerable young teeth. Think of the packet as a *toy*. The experience of throwing food away should stop you doing this sort of thing too often.

• You could fill the packet with something else, such as (in the case of cereals) crumbled Weetabix ('or All-bran, so they never ask for it again!'). This tactic is best for young children; with older children, you could be quite frank: 'The stuff inside is too sugary, but I *could* buy the packet and put your usual cereal in. OK?' At least you'll only have to buy the packet once.

• Another idea is to let your child (or help your child) make their own hilarious/scary/crazy/pretty cereal packet at home: cover an old cereal box with plain paper and then let your child create their own packet design using coloured or shiny paper, fabric pieces, paint and glue. Perhaps stick on big buttons for eyes or wool for hair. The more the result is the child's own ideas and work the more they will feel it's theirs and want to use it. Stuff it with crumpled newspaper while it's being worked on.

When it's done, smooth clingfilm over it to keep the artwork intact and put in your usual cereal. Now your child has the pleasure of using their own special packet.

• Similarly, fill up drinks bottles with fruit juice and yoghurt pots with your own fruit yoghurt so your child can enjoy the containers.

DON'T YOU LOVE OUR FIZZY ADVERTS!!

Obesity, diabetes and sugar

Children are getting fatter. In England, 13.5% of girls and 9% of boys are now overweight. (In the US it's even worse – 25% of children are overweight, with over 10% officially obese.) The figures climb steadily, year on year. Further, Type-2 ('maturity onset') diabetes, a first cousin of obesity, which previously afflicted older adults, is now, almost unbelievably, attacking teenagers.

Excess sugar consumption is being blamed for this disastrous situation. The thing is, sugar is very calorie-dense but not 'filling', so it is extremely easy to over-consume. It is easy to be unaware that cereals can be almost half sugar, a small pot of fruit yoghurt can contain five teaspoons of sugar, while a can of fizzy drink can have almost eleven! 21% of British 7-10 year-olds get through nearly 10 cans of fizzy drink a week.

Fizzy drinks create other problems – they seem to make some children uncontrollable. Schools which have banned the sale of fizzy drinks report an almost instant improvement in children's behaviour. And as well as causing tooth decay, our huge consumption of sugar and other refined carbohydrates has been linked to a variety of conditions including constipation, haemorrhoids, appendicitis, diverticulitis, some cancers and heart disease.

But who chiefly buys sugared and fizzy goods? Parents, it seems: for example, at least eight out of ten cans of fizzy drinks are bought by parents for consumption at home.

Message: be informed and shop to keep your child well. *Plain water* is the best drink for a child – or anyone. Make it the norm. If children say they want a drink but reject plain water, they are probably not thirsty.

"Which of your treats is healthier, Granny?
E423, modified starch, BHA and Aspartame,
or E369, hydrogenated fat, MSG and permitted colouring??"

HOW TO SURVIVE OTHER CHILDREN, OTHER ADULTS, OTHER PLACES

As if coping with advertisers, manufacturers and supermarkets wasn't enough, there's also the matter of parents with other ideas and children whose food horizons stretch no further than burgers and fish fingers. Trying to remain polite *and* sticking to your principles can be tricky, and dealing with parties, presents, visits and outings with some other children (and their parents) can feel like taking an entrance exam for the diplomatic service.

And then there are all the problems of trying to find a child something healthy when you go out: in a café, a restaurant, a station – and even at sports clubs, where they might be expected to do better. Should you complain? Is it even worth asking for fresh fruit or a drink of plain water, and getting a blank stare or even a rebuke, or the ubiquitous 'everybody else seems to like it' or 'no one else has complained'?

> " My son is only eight months old and already has had gifts of chocolate. Other people have criticised my 'Strictly no sugar' rule, but why on earth give a *baby* processed sugar?
>
> I understand I'll have to reassess the situation when he is older and he starts asking for sweets, but we're not at that stage yet!"
>
> "My local chemist's shop sells *sweets* of all things! *And* they put them at the front of the counter, right at child eye-level. When I complained I was told I was cruel!"

On the other hand, there are good experiences to be had – an accommodating restaurant, meeting like-minded parents or children who are good role models for your own, good market stalls, finding home-grown, organic food in a local shop, and the biggest boost of all: observing your own child choosing to eat something that you would have chosen yourself!

Sweet tips:

• Make a plan for sweet and chocolate-eating. It is both unfair and impractical to ban them completely, but you can limit them to certain clearly-defined situations (see *A very sweet tip* opposite).

• Never give sweets before a meal, only afterwards, because sugar is an appetite depressant. Of course appetite will return, but if it does so when the meal is over, what use is that?

• If someone offers your child sweets, you can both simply say thank you and take them home. There's no rule of etiquette that says they must be eaten there and then.

• Brushing teeth after sweet-eating is not advised: the acid-producing effect of the sugar makes the tooth enamel vulnerable for a while. Scrubbing it in this vulnerable state does more harm than good. On the other hand, following sweets with something alkali such as a small piece

of cheese or a drink of milk counteracts the acid and protects the enamel.

• You can still try to influence what your child eats even when she goes to stay with a friend. Someone I know would give the friend's mother a big bar of fruit and nut chocolate and say 'I hope you don't mind, but if you were thinking of letting them have sweets, I would prefer they had this. I think it's less harmful than some other kinds of sweets.' Whatever the merits of fruit and nut chocolate, she made a clear statement about the limits of sweet-eating. She also said that the other parent always seemed relieved to have the sweet situation settled.

A very sweet tip

This is the best tip I've heard for dealing with sweet-eating. It came from the mother of a five year-old boy who had perfect, gleaming white teeth – yet he sometimes talked about which sweets he liked. What was his mother's secret? She said she had a routine: every Sunday, after lunch, he was allowed two sweets. This was the only time he was allowed them. She said that if someone gave him some sweets she said she would exclaim 'Oh how lovely! You'll enjoy having these on Sunday!' And on Sunday, the sweets would be brought out and he would choose two. If the donated sweets accumulated too much, she would quietly dispose of some. I think this is clever stuff:

- The mother protected her child's teeth by keeping sweets to a minimum, and without going into the business of banning them.

- She had a simple and clear cut plan that her son could understand and which was easy to remember and stick to.

- She allowed sweets only after a meal, when her son's blood sugar was high and he would be unlikely to want more.

- She and her son could warmly thank the people who gave the sweets, but by saying 'you'll enjoy these on Sunday' made it clear that she had a routine in place and that the sweets were not going to be opened before then – even to please the giver.

- She made the whole plan seem like a treat!

- She stayed in charge. She didn't allow someone else to sabotage what she wanted for her child.

> I think this is a good example of making an easy, practicable
> plan, sticking to it and not upsetting anyone. Perhaps as her
> son gets older he might eat more sweets, but the early years
> are the most crucial, and that, fortunately, is when parents
> have the most control.

Avoiding junk

There probably isn't any way of completely avoiding it, but at least
it is possible to do so most of the time. The more your children are used
to good home cooked fare, the better the chances of their being
disappointed (even disgusted) with the taste and texture and smell of
junk.

• Instead of giving your child chicken nuggets, roast a tray of small
chicken drumsticks for your children to eat as finger food. However, if a
young child is familiar with 'Chicken-Licken' and other such stories and
might make the connection between Chicken-Licken and the chicken leg
in her hand, just use the word 'drumstick'; or remove the bones after
cooking. Leg meat is much more tasty and juicy that chicken breasts, and
will be sweeter for having been cooked on the bone. Roast a batch and
freeze the spares (see page 160).

> "Why do parents complain 'he won't eat anything else,' or
> 'she'll only eat so-and-so.'? Who *gave* the children this stuff
> in the first place? Children don't put the dinner on the
> table! If children have never had the so-and-so at home they
> won't expect it.'

Of course, if you have already bought your child nuggets, you
might have to cope with possible requests for them – although a hand-
held drumstick may be instantly preferred. However, the trick is to (a)
phase nuggets out very gradually over many weeks, and (b) make sure
your drumsticks are tasty and fun to eat. Perhaps roast them in a little
honey, or serve them with tomato sauce for dipping. Also roast chicken

wings. They are fiddly to eat and take a pleasantly long, messy time to get through – an activity meal!

• Similarly, make your own 'fish fingers' (see page 149).

• Tell your children what goes on behind the scenes in some fast food outlets. If you'd like to find out more yourself or want more ammunition, try reading Eric Schlosser's *Fast Food Nation* (see page 142).

• Make burgers at home from the best, organic minced beef. Eat with any trimmings the children like (see page 165).The idea is for them to feel disappointed with commercial ones – and the amount they get – when they go out for a burger.

• Feed excellent burgers to your children's friends if they are burger fans – let them see how much better yours are – and free to them! Great prestige for your child – and you're indirectly helping other parents also. Give them a good milk-shake too (see page 173). If they'd rather keep coming to you than to a burger bar...perhaps you can come to some financial arrangement with them! Or perhaps you'd just rather have them come to you anyway so you get to know your child's friends, where they all are and what they're doing. Perhaps they could join in and help make the burgers.

• One mother said she always encouraged her children's friends to come to her house to eat – and also to cook things: burgers, pizzas, anything they wanted. This way, she said, not only did she get to know her children's friends, but she learned a lot of other things too! And she knew where her children were, as well as what they were eating.

The dreaded request - sorted

"My friend's eight-year-old has just started pestering to go to McD's. They've told her all about nutrition and animal welfare, but made sure she was involved in the decision instead of just being told 'no'. They said she could go if she wanted to, but... she must pay for it herself out of her pocket money.

"When she went, she was surprised to find how much the whole 'meal' cost. Her parents were then able to talk to her about how 'free gifts' aren't actually free after all, and how she's helping to pay for all the advertising that she sees on TV. Apparently she's now going round telling all her friends how they're being ripped off!"

"My son pestered me to take him to a burger restaurant because 'everyone else goes'. In the end, I told him we would go once, so he could say he had been, but that would be all – we wouldn't go again. So we went to our local Burger King and he ordered a huge burger and a fizzy drink. It was more than he could manage really, but he didn't want to give up, so he ate and ate until he was sick. And guess what, he's never asked to go again!"

"Both my children dislike these burger places. They prefer to have a 'posh' baguette sandwich or fish and chips when we go out."

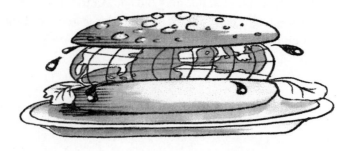

"My sons, six and three said, quite voluntarily, that they didn't want to go to McD's any more (I'd taken them after much pestering). They left *all* the food, except the milk-shake, and said it tasted horrible! What a revelation!"

"My son pestered me to take him to McDonald's because he's seen other children with the toys and things. But when we went, he was surprised to find it selling food – he thought he was going to a toy shop!"

The best fast food

• The best fast food is probably fish and chips, and that's something you really can't do authentically at home. Make that a 'treat' meal rather than a burger and 'fries'. Fish-shop chips are bigger and therefore less fatty than fries, and there's usually more to eat in a helping. And, of course, there's fish – and mushy peas for mushy pea fans!

• Some high-street pizzas are actually not bad – indeed, one or two are extremely good, although they can charge gourmet prices. Find the best in your area (ask around), and eat with plenty of salad.

• There is really no need ever to cook chips at home so be happy for them to be seen as a treat when you go out. (As chips are *always* available when you eat out, this could be seen as a real treat – and you won't worry that you child is having too many.) However, if your child is really hankering after them over a period of time, then roast some frozen oven chips occasionally. But do make sauté potatoes from time to time, which although also a bit fatty, can actually be nicer than commercial frozen chips and may be preferred (see page 155). Of course they are much cheaper, too – no 'added value'. For the best flavour, cook them in goose fat, now available in supermarkets. (Surprisingly, goose fat is polyunsaturated. Take a piece from the freezer, and watch it melt into a puddle on a saucer!)

Drinks

• In a nutshell, sugary drinks rot teeth and those with artificial sweeteners can erode tooth enamel. Both, of course are disastrous. Dentists know when the tooth damage has been caused by drinks because it is then that the *front* teeth get spoiled as the drink washes over them. 'No added sugar' and 'reduced sugar' usually mean that one or more artificial sweeteners have been added, along with citric acid, which erodes tooth enamel. Some drinks have both sugar and sweeteners.

• Unfortunately, fresh fruit juice is also damaging to teeth as it contains both sugar and acid. Therefore, juice should be very diluted and it is recommended that it should be drunk only at mealtimes so the food can further dilute it.

When you are out and canned drinks are the only ones available, try to keep them for when you are eating. Always carry a small water bottle with you. If you fill water bottles up and leave them unstoppered overnight, most of the chlorine will have evaporated by morning and the water will taste nicer. As for mineral waters, some have too many minerals for children and can be quite salty.

• No 'eating in' establishment should refuse you a glass of plain water – free. Pubs and bars *never* refuse water, and often have a water jug (and ice) on the counter.

> "My daughter pestered me for a fake orange drink. So I got some, emptied it away and put in orange juice. I keep refilling it with juice. She doesn't know."
>
> "I thought Sunny Delight was just orange juice until someone showed me the label! I was utterly horrified. I showed the label to my daughter and said we'd been tricked. And that was the end of it in our house."

• If there is the choice, go for a milkshake, or ask for tea *and* a jug of hot water to make the tea very weak for your children. (Hot water is free, and ad lib. If they can make tea they can make hot water.) Pick up extra milk

114

tubs or, if there is fresh milk, ask for a jugful (maybe not free) to make the tea nicer. See if there is hot chocolate available.

• Always read the label of any bottled drink. As a rough guideline, the word 'drink' on a label means you don't want it.

Suitable for children?

"It is so disappointing to eat out with children, 'children's menus' are appalling – it's all chips, burgers, sausages, nuggets ....*everywhere*. If you ask for anything else, such as a small portion of adult food, you just get a blank stare."

"I'd like to throw every 'children's menu' into the bin – along with the food!"

"I was horrified to find sweets on sale at the swimming baths. You would think they would know better."

"Why is it that 'children's menus' always have food of a much poorer quality that on the adult menu?"

"My children will happily eat anything we eat – marinated fish, vegetable couscous, etc. None of them would touch anything on a 'kiddies' menu."

"There's an assumption that children need 'children's food'. Why?"

"Some places are accommodating – usually small independent places, but they are hard to find."

"I find Italian restaurants are the most accommodating. There's *one* menu for all, which is how it should be I think. There's no 'us' and 'them' (i.e. the children)!"

" I find that Chinese, Indian or Italian restaurants are best for taking children to – they don't have 'children's menus'!"

"We go to pubs that have adult food only or small, independent places. Bella Pasta and other Italian places are good and also Rick Stein's 'bistro' restaurant. My children love to choose Indian curry or dim sum. They've never been to a burger bar."

"My children love going out for a summertime afternoon tea in country places. It's a very civilized meal. Of course they eat lots of scones and cake so it's a *real* treat, and the cakes are usually home-made too. I think these are good places to take children to eat."

Several parents have remarked how much easier it was to get good food for children abroad – apparently everywhere in Europe except the UK. Small servings of adult food were usually available. 'Italian restaurants are the best for feeding children!' wrote one mother. Someone else wrote about a Swiss 'children's meal': three courses, full of vegetables and fruit'. Some one else told of the bowl of cherries given to a child for dessert in Switzerland. As parents said: why not here?

• When you go out, it helps to take your own food with you. Sandwiches are usually the best option, and a roll holds up better than slices of bread. If you make a cheese sandwich, moisten it well with, for example, lots of very thin (and chopped) cucumber slices, or a little chutney, so the sandwich isn't dry and hard to get through. Always have some 'nibbles' of dried fruit and such to give a weary child a little pick-up. Older children could make their own sandwiches and choose what to put in them.

• In restaurants, tell the waiter not to bring the children's menu. With a young child, ask for an extra plate (or use your side plate) and share your own portion. With several children, divide adult portions among them. "This is how mine first had Peking duck, stir fries and waldorf salad," said one mother. "And I compliment them on being sophisticated!"

• Try not to rely on finding anything suitable to eat at all. Go prepared! If there is something nice, do compliment the staff to encourage them. With large outfits, or when the manager isn't around, consider writing a letter telling them how pleased you were, and why.

• Conversely, if it's terrible, write and tell the management how angry you are – and precisely why. Of course, you could spend much time writing such letters... but, on the other hand, sometimes letters of complaint get taken seriously, especially if several arrive on the same topic. Also, sometimes the top management might not *know* what a particular outlet or employee has been up to and could be very interested to learn. In cases like this, action may well be taken – you may even get to hear about it and possibly get a refund.

Peer pressures

Children often pressure other children to eat junk. Below are a few parents' comments. See also pages 123 and 124, and 136.

> "Give children the confidence and power to avoid peer pressure on everything – not just food. When they have a decision to make, encourage them to think for themselves, and practise with them saying 'No, I don't want one' out loud so they have practised it before they need to do it for real. This could also stand them in good stead for refusing cigarettes, drugs and alcohol later on..."
>
> " 95% of the other children at her playgroup take food (packed lunches) that I'd prefer my child not to eat, so she feels different. So now, she asks for things she's seen on television."
>
> "At my child's playschool, birthday sweets are regularly given out to all the children as they go home. They now let my son out early so he doesn't see them. It's very odd that I seem to be the only parent who feels like this."

> "I am truly appalled at what other parents send their children to school with for lunch. But because so many children have this terrible food, my child is in the minority and so now these parents have given me a problem with my child."
>
> "Teenagers especially want to eat what their friends have when they are with them. They want to know what the food is, and they want to join in. But you can always serve really super stuff at home, and then not worry too much. I know they can go out and buy food with their pocket money, but you choose how much money they get. They won't want to use up too much when they can eat free at home."

Grandparents and others

There can be a very special rapport between young and old. Grandparents may have more time for rambling conversations with children, and can fulfil a useful role in listening to them. Children can be fascinated to hear 'family history' tales and also delight in having a patient, interested audience for their own thoughts. And grandparents who dispense warm welcomes, hugs and kisses are worth their weight in gold. Also, as more mothers go out to work, many grandparents are playing an increasingly crucial role in children's lives. In some cases, it is at their grandparents' house that children have their only experience of home cooking.

Treats given by grandparents can seem very special – some of their special home-made bread, or apples from their trees, or giant, sweet 'Golden drop' gooseberries off their bush. Cooking at grandma's can be a great treat. But what happens when grandparents (and other relatives) do the opposite, and actually undermine parents' good principles? What is to be done?

118

• Look at how often the problem occurs and ask yourself if it's worth even mentioning it. Preserving good relations in a situation that involves children is very well worth doing.

> "My children turned their noses up at broccoli until they had it at Nanna's house – and now they can't get enough of it!"
>
> "My daughter (12) refused to learn to cook at home, but she does it with her Nan. She's very proud now because she knows 'how to do a whole dinner!'"

• If something is becoming – or has become – a routine, such as a sweets every time they come, and they come often, you may feel you must do something. One idea is the 'sweet solution' on page 109, of course telling the grandparents your routine and why you have it. If this makes them realize that most of their sweets cannot possibly get eaten, you can say, truthfully, that the child will choose and *some* of them certainly will be eaten and enjoyed very much. Whether they continue to buy sweets is up to them, but that has nothing to do with your routine. You are the parent, this is your child, and you are in charge.

• Do be ready to discuss it – indeed show them how informed you are, and that this is a serious decision based on facts and the best interests of your child. Try not to get angry – you are, in fact, rejecting their gifts, however unsuitable, and they cannot feel happy about that. But make it clear it's only the sweets you are rejecting, not the people, nor their right to bring gifts.

• Perhaps suggest other things that the child might enjoy – a book, new crayons, a comical India rubber, a notebook, a shuttlecock and bat, knitting or sewing things, a puzzle...or is there some activity they could do with your children that you cannot for some reason?

• If it's feasible, blame yourself for not being clear about it all earlier, changing your mind, or whatever and apologize – but stick to your guns.

• In the end, it's up to you. Your child's health is your responsibility.

• With other adults, the general advice is much the same, and keeping good relations with, for example, your children's friends and their parents is worth a bit of effort.

• When other children come to your house for a meal, provide the same good food as you normally do, but provide choices, so it's not 'all or nothing'. Have a pleasant meal. Don't criticise the other children's eating habits or allow your children to do so during the visit.

> "I never had any trouble feeding other people's children. I did keep a few fish fingers in the freezer in case of emergency, but never needed them"
>
> "I enjoyed putting on a feast for my daughter and her friends. I would put out a mixture of things to eat: slices of chicken, sautéed potatoes, stuffing balls, a few good sausages, peas, chops, drumsticks, grilled apple slices, baby meatballs, bacon rolls, sweetcorn fritters, scrambled egg ... not all at once! But several items at a time on serving dishes and they would help themselves. It all went! I'd put out a few fish fingers as well so there was something familiar.
>
> "Afterwards I'd do grilled fruit – always popular, or Scotch pancakes, or make apple fritters, the number one favourite."
>
> "My children can be horrified by what they're given at other children's houses. I have to tell them not to criticise. I say 'When you are in someone else's house, you have to eat what you are given.' (But I'm always very keen to hear all about it when they get home!)"
>
> "When my five year-old's friend came to tea, her mother's suggestion was nuggets, fish fingers and sausages. But my daughter had chosen the tea she wanted for her: her favourite pasta sauce, mixed salad, followed by apple sauce. Where do you go?"

"Children who are used to rubbish at home are not so keen to try good, healthier food when offered it."

"I don't think parents [who feed junk] realize they are actually *preventing* their children from liking normal food."

HOW TO MAKE GOOD PACKED LUNCHES

A t last! It's time for a break – and time to open the lunch box and see what Mum's put in it. Now what is there today? Well, what has Mum (it's usually Mum) put in? Of course you (Mum) want the food to be as healthy as possible, but if your child doesn't like it it won't get eaten. (You may or may not ever know whether it was.) It should also look tempting.

What goes into the lunch box, however, may be modified by what other children take – 'peer pressure'. The pressure is usually to take poorer quality food rather than better, although sometimes pressure to bring junk is reversed: One mother said:

> 'The other children would come to see what my daughter had got. They were very envious – she became a bit of a star! I was surprised because I'd just tried to make the food interesting. It wasn't a lot of work: I mass-produced most of it at the start of the week and each morning I quickly chose a bit of this and a bit of that.'

Nevertheless, whatever the other children eat, your child won't want to appear too different. One father said 'I'm not going to sacrifice my child on the altar of my principles', and it's a point: the parent doesn't have to deal with the situation in school; the child does.

Tips on dealing with peer pressure

• Stick to your guns but compromise a bit so your child doesn't feel too different. For example, it's not fair to make your child the only one in the class who never has crisps.

• Teach them to reply. I once heard a six year-old say 'So what are you eating then? Loada junk! Doesn't your mum know anything?'

• Can you persuade the parents of your child's friends to send healthy food too? A group of 'healthy eaters' sitting together is less vulnerable – and reinforcing.

• Make it look so attractive that other children are intrigued – you might start a trend.

• Involve your children in choosing some of the food – they know what's 'in' and can stop you embarrassing them.

> "I give each of my three children (aged 11, and twins aged 8) two pounds to buy food for their lunch boxes. They choose exotic fruit, yoghurt, crackers, raisins and small cheeses, and award themselves one 'treat' item."

Tips on what to put in

Some of these tips are more suitable for younger children, some for older ones. Also, schools vary, so it's worth finding out what would be best for your own child's situation.

• Don't give yourself tons of extra work! Mass produce when possible: for example, you could cut up all the vegetables at the start of the week, store in cold water in the fridge and pack a few each day. Older children could help – if you can persuade them to.

• Make a list of 'lunch-box possibilities' – things you know your child likes, and go down the list. Incorporate the items for the week on your weekly shopping list so you know you've got everything.

• Eating at school can be rushed, either because of time or because children want to dash out to play. Things that take a lot of chewing could just be abandoned.

• Where will the lunch boxes be kept at school? If it's near hot water pipes or radiators mention this to your child's teacher. In any case, think which foods will survive the journey and storage.

• Have several different things for your child to eat, not just one or two.

• Put each item in its own container, so your child has to open them one by one to see what there is. You will need some small plastic containers – and hope that most will find their way home, but also save any small containers and re-usable wrappings from foods you buy. The miniature jam jars and tubs that are put out in hotels and cafés can also be useful. Put in plastic cutlery as necessary and perhaps a paper towel if the food could be messy to eat.

• A miniature flask is useful for hot drinks or soup in winter and cold ones in summer.

Planning the food

Plan for a balance as much as you can, which is to say, include a good helping of a protein food (cold meat, smoked or tinned fish, cheese, hard-boiled egg, or a vegetarian combination such as beans and bread or a rice and peas salad), some carbohydrate (bread, or a portion of rice or a potato, or a pasta salad) and some fruit, vegetables or salad items.

Put in:

• things that have to be opened – pea pods to pop, a satsuma to peel, a hard-boiled egg to shell and a tiny twist of salt-and-pepper to undo

• slices of salami, varying them from time to time; strips of ham, tongue or haslet

• cheese cut into sticks, slices or cubes. Vary the type of cheese, mostly avoiding processed cheese because of its poorer nutritional value, although you could occasionally include one of the 'pick-&-mix' cheese portions for variety – and because of its wrapping

• pieces of ham wrapped around cheese sticks

• at least one special thing, perhaps a giant strawberry, a 'two-legged' carrot, a samosa, a bhaji, a spring roll, or one special surprise

• sugar-free oatcakes with cheese and grapes

• a chicken drumstick or wings

• slices or roll-ups of any cold meat

• a sausage, perhaps vegetarian, perhaps in a wholewheat bap

• sandwiches cut into triangles or fingers, varying the bread (see page 171)

• use frozen bread for sandwiches! It will be thawed by lunchtime but it will keep the filling cold and the sandwiches will keep their shape

• filled rolls, baps or buns

• miniature jars or tubs of mustard, chutney or pickle, perhaps with an ice-cream spatula

• filled pitta pocket or a tortilla 'wrap'

• a bagel with cream cheese and ham or salmon

- potato salad (add chopped cucumber, spring onion, bacon bits and mayonnaise); a rice or pasta salad

- little packs of dried fruit – no-cook apricots, unsulphured apricots, figs, golden sultanas, tropical dried fruits; sometimes a mixture

- a fruit muffin, or a slice of carrot cake, banana bread; a buttered scone, perhaps with a slice of cheese in it

- a fruit loaf and Cheddar cheese sandwich; a slice of fruit cake with a thick slice of cheese

- a container of plain popcorn, perhaps home-popped – nice explosive fun!

- any leftover food that is good cold, such as pizza, quiche, pie, roast chicken or a rice dish

- bread sticks, and perhaps a dip or two

- a small carton of plain, organic yoghurt and a plastic spoon, or mix the yoghurt with chopped fresh fruit and a pinch of sugar

- fruit: a bunchlet of grapes, or two bunchlets of different colours; orange segments, sprigs of red, white or black currants in a box; mango slices, diced papaya, any whole smaller fruits, varying them through the season – lychees and kumquats in winter, loganberries and greengages in summer, for example

> " My two teenage boys have flagged up that it's not 'cool' to be seen munching raw carrot sticks (or raw anything)! But it doesn't seem to be a problem with the girls. "

- sometimes just one kind of fruit, particularly if it's something special like strawberries or cherries, but mostly two; wrap each type of fruit separately to preserve the surprise element

- if you think a whole apple or orange will take too long to eat, send a half one, possibly cut up; push the pieces together and wrap tightly

- a supermarket packet of ready-mixed fruit snacks for picnics

- very small vegetables and fruits: baby carrots, miniature sweetcorn, very small red peppers, small bananas, cherry tomatoes, radishes, clementines

- raw vegetables cut into thin sticks, small cubes or chunks. Bright colours are more attractive

- perhaps add a dip for vegetable sticks or tacos; you could make your own based on a mixture of yoghurt and crème fraîche

> "I sent for a 'Scooby Doo lunch box' from a website. It contained a sugary drink, four small biscuits and a tub of processed cheese. None of my three would touch it."
>
> "How can anyone call Lunchables a lunch?!"

- for over-fives, a few nuts, perhaps in a twist of foil or in a little pot: cashews, Brazils, walnuts; or seeds: sunflower seeds or green pumpkin seeds; a few plump olives if your child likes them

- for over-fives, make up a little packet of mixed nuts, seeds and sultanas

- vegetables cut into different shapes and patterns; for example give radishes and cucumber chunks teeth! – i.e. cut them in half, zigzag fashion – very amusing for young children; similarly, halve a zig-zag-cut orange

- spring onion tassels and radish roses (cut them the night before and leave them in cold water to curl)

Drinks

- Have a couple of different kinds for variety and choice. Filling plastic bottles from larger containers at home is the most economical. Fill one with plain water if none is provided, perhaps adding a dash of fruit juice to colour it; perhaps enclose a straw to unwrap and insert.

- Sometimes include a ring-pull can of juice as a novelty.

- Buy little cartons of pure (unsweetened) fruit juice which come with a straw attached.

- Perhaps send a flask of *'café crème'* in a miniature flask – iced in summer and hot in winter (see page 87) for a nutritious and welcome drink, either cooling or warming.

- In cold weather, fill a miniature flask with hot soup. Pack a wholewheat roll to eat with it. In summer, send iced soup complete with ice cubes in it.

- Send iced milk. Make some milk ice-cubes and drop one or two into the milk just before the child leaves.

- Send a milk shake, perhaps with a straw. This is useful for older children who might think plain milk is babyish, for example:

- make a little cocoa and top it up with cold milk

- purée some red summer fruit and mix with the milk – if it's not red enough, add a drop of beetroot juice, or purée a very little beetroot with the fruit. (This is what some manufacturers do to make food look fruitier!)

- purée a banana, adding vanilla and nutmeg; a miniscule pinch of turmeric will make it a deeper yellow without affecting the taste (another factory-food trick – usually to make something look creamier)

- 'witch's brew': puréed blackberries or black currants for a purple drink!

- Make – or let the children make – a smoothie for their lunch box.

> "I often ask my two what other children take for their packed lunches, partly out of curiosity, partly as a useful way for us to talk about food, and partly to get ideas. One day, this conversation occurred:
>
> 'Oh, and P__ of course brought cheese strings and Hula Hoops and Ribena and a choc bar.'
>
> 'Is that *all*? Didn't he have a sandwich or anything?'
>
> 'Oh yes, he had a sandwich, but he put it in the bin.'

"I'm doing joined-up writing already!"

HOW TO DEAL WITH SCHOOLS AND NURSERIES

> "The problem with school food was that it was not under the department of education, even though it was provided in educational establishments and teachers organised and supervised the mealtimes. It came under 'health' and was therefore, officially, not part of children's education. That, ultimately, was its downfall."
>
> *Former education officer.*

Since the abolition of the nutritional requirement for school dinners in the 1980's, the standard has plummeted. In April 2001, the government reintroduced a minimum standard, but unfortunately, this is *very* minimum. It allows, for example, soft and diet drinks to be provided in nursery schools! Monitoring it is a problem in itself.

School heads (and nursery managers), along with their governors, are responsible for the food on their premises. They are responsible for drawing up contracts with caterers, and checking that the minimum specification has been met. But heads did not choose, and usually do not enjoy, this new, non-teaching job, and are not trained in either nutrition or catering. Also, schools must now balance their own budgets, and most heads find there is never enough money for what they would like to do. School meals therefore now compete with books, computers, teacher hours, swimming lessons – and everything else.

When school meals are poor

Teachers have always been taught 'health education' at college, but this chiefly covers children's general physical development, hygiene, childhood diseases and so on and I have not heard of a college that has made much of the problems caused by junk foods and their ilk. Therefore, teachers have not been trained to think about the current very serious food issues. Indeed, they may eat badly themselves, or at any rate, no better than any one else. Unless a teacher has a personal interest in food, there could be no one on a school's staff who is at all informed or interested in this area, or who has to be.

However, when school food is poor, you, as parents, have every right to complain – and the more parents do so the better:

* Talk to the head directly (but see 'complaining to a school', below)

If you wish, and quite independently of the school, you can also go and see your local authority's 'Client Officer' and read the contract the school has. Client officers deal directly with caterers and have a legal duty to see that the contract specification is being met.

* Contact *The Health Education Trust,* which can set up a School Nutrition Action Group, which brings parents together with the school's teachers and catering staff, local health workers and children. It is also very worthwhile getting the Trust's advice on the whole subject of tackling poor school food. *The chips are down* is also very well worth reading (see page 140 and 143).

* Talk to the Parent Governor(s) to try to get the subject onto the policy agenda of the school management team. Success is more likely if several parents request it.

* If the school has a Parent Teachers Association, get them to support you.

* Try to find out what other schools do – there may be ideas you can suggest.

* It's best if schools have a 'whole school' food policy, integrating teaching, school meals and snacks. Schools can choose to belong to a government scheme, The Healthy Schools Standard, which works towards this.

*The *Grab 5!* project at *Sustain,* and *The Food Dudes* can both offer support and, sometimes, practical in-school sessions for children on eating well (see page 140).

* You could also talk to your local authority's health promotion department and community dietician. They can help create healthy eating policies and arrange talks for parents.

"I am a school cook and I can turn a school around in three weeks – all through the pricing. For example, portions of chips are small but expensive, while jacket potatoes are cheaper and big; vegetables are cheap and you get a lot, while a piece of cake is expensive and tiny. I watch the children lining up, hungry, and counting their money. They soon work out what to choose to fill up without being spent up! But it's essential to have a cooperative head."

"In the nursery where I work, the biggest problem with food is the ignorance of the parents. Children *will* try healthy foods, but the parents say they won't!"

Complaining to a school

* First, do note that schools are now under unprecedented pressures of many kinds, and also that they are well used to parental complaints which can range from valid to ludicrous, vague to physically abusive. Demonstrate your seriousness and rationality.

* Check your facts. It seems that children grumble about school food almost universally, even when it's good, so get them to be precise. Perhaps ask other parents or other children. Does the school post a menu? You will have more confidence when you know your facts are correct and other parents agree with you.

* Speak directly to the head (or nursery manager). Don't try to drum up support from other members of staff first, which is asking them to be

disloyal, although of course you could mention the matter. Ask or phone for a private word 'sometime', so it's a good time for both of you.

* Don't go while you are feeling angry. You're more likely to do it badly and you might say things you'd later regret. Your good relationship with the people who care for your child is important. Think out a pleasant approach.

* Don't write a letter. It's too formal and could seem like an attack.

* When you go, smile and start pleasantly; say something positive about the nursery/school.

* Then say there is one area that bothers you, and say, concisely, what it is. Don't ramble on. Sum up your complaint and give one or two examples, if appropriate.

"I've had my pester-power snack and now I'm ready to be a pest."

* Say exactly what you would like done, such as the replacement of sugary snacks by something healthier (such as fresh fruit), or the removal of 'fast food' meals at midday. Say why, briefly. You could mention the damage done to young teeth by the regular doses of sugar or the effect of additives on behaviour (see page 95), or the long-term risks to health posed by the daily exposure to fatty, processed, mass-produced fare. You could mention the gradual and insidious undermining of healthy eating habits by such food. And in an educational establishment!

* Then finish by repeating how pleased you are with other aspects.

The reply will probably be an explanation of why things are as they are. Don't expect instant agreement or an immediate promise to do what you want.

Listen carefully to the reply, ask for further information or clarification if you wish, but try not to get into an argument. Perhaps take notes. Keep it pleasant, agree to leave the matter with them, thank them and leave. The head will need to think about your request and perhaps consult other people.

Wait. If changes do occur, be quick to say how delighted you are. If nothing happens, give a reminder. Of course, it can help if there are other parents saying the same thing.

No luck? Then try other approaches, as above.

Whole school or one class?

If your child's teacher allows parents to bring sweets or cakes on their children's birthday, it could be just her personal decision, so speak to her first. If she insists it's fine, then go to the head teacher. If you start by going over her head she could well feel slighted. (Courteously asking parents to send a little fresh fruit – if anything – for a young child's birthday can work extremely well. It should be a whole-school policy to do this.)

If you have worries over the content of 'food technology' lessons, approach the head of department, but know that food firms are filling the funding gap here and they influence the syllabus. Pupils' assignments are often about 'designing' food for retail sale, and this can displace practical cooking entirely. Don't be surprised if the teachers feel their hands are tied.

Packed lunches

"Peer pressure' to eat junk at school is a massive source of parental anger. If schools issued firm guidelines to parents about what they would and would not accept, the problem could be solved. Some schools do this. However, because a few parents can take enormous offence at this ('Don't tell me how to feed my child!') schools often tread carefully. The tack for schools to take is not that they are telling parents 'how to feed' their children, but what is least problematical on school premises.

Sample guidelines for packed meals

The school can say it:

• doesn't allow any kind of drinks – they are sticky, they get spilled and create a variety of problems. Either water and beakers will be provided, or parents can send plain water.

• doesn't allow any type of chocolate or other confectionary: also sticky and problematical

• would like children to end their meal with fruit

Water

Schools should provide access to water, but because of their existing buildings and plumbing it's not always easy. The only drinking fountains are probably in the toilets, or in the playground where certain children can take delight in soaking anyone foolish or forgetful enough to go anywhere near them, resulting in their being turned off.

Schools should seriously try to make water available at mid-day at least. In the days of universal school dinner provision all schools used to provide water jugs and beakers. Meanwhile, parents should be able – indeed encouraged – to send a small bottle of water.

Snacks

Some schools operate a 'Fresh fruit only' policy for any food brought to school for break times. The fruit can be left in the child's bag, or, with younger children, put in a 'fruit basket' until break time. It's easy for the teacher to give the fruit out if each child's piece of fruit is inside a paper bag with their name on it. If she says 'No name, no fruit', the problem quickly solves itself. Any other foods are simply returned with a (courteous) reminder.

This is an easy and practical way of both encouraging children to eat fruit and also of keeping out less desirable types of food. It is usually very popular with parents too, so a school should have few qualms about introducing it.

Crisps for computers!

One school head (at least) had the answer: she simply told parents 'Either you can spend £1,000 on crisps or I can pass the hat round. I know which I'd prefer, but it's up to you'. She got the money. Actually, schools *hate* collecting and counting all those greasy packets, and it takes up masses of ancillary staff hours and storage space.

It is also financially odd – much more money needs to be spent on crisps than what the new computer would cost to buy!

Drinks machines

These can be a source of much needed income for schools, but when the contract is up for renewal, the head could ask the company to put in a mixture of drinks, including milk and water. There are also companies that supply machines that dispense milk and other healthy drinks (see page 140), and water dispensers have also made profits.

One retired teacher, now doing supply teaching said: 'I doubt if schools are actually in pocket over Cola machines and such. The sugar and caffeine send the kids sky high, and are one of the major reasons for disruptive behaviour and teacher stress. The stress results in teachers taking days off when they feel they just can't cope – and then the school has to pay for people like me to keep filling in. I'd guess schools are making an overall loss.'

Other countries

It is interesting to compare our provision with that of other countries:

"Here in France (Angoulême), my children always get a four course meal every day at school: starter, main dish, cheese and dessert. There are always vegetables or a salad. They have to take something for each course, although I think a bit of swapping goes on afterwards. I can hardly believe that the British Government actually removed the requirement for meals to be nutritious, and that now your children are given chips and burgers and unhealthy things like that. Why didn't the parents take to the streets?"

"In my school in Germany, we all took our lunches. We took good dark rye bread – you can't get that in London – with cheese or ham, and then an apple or a banana. At the beginning of each week we would choose the sort of milk we wanted to drink: chocolate, plain, banana or some other flavour. Then at the right time, two children would go down to the cellar to fetch the milk and we would all have it.

"If someone arrived with a can of Coke or with a Mars bar, then the teacher would ring up the parents and tell them off! The teacher would say 'This sort of thing is not good for your child to have.' But it hardly ever happened. People just sent ordinary good food. Of course we only had a very short break so food wasn't really ever an issue."

"I am horrified at the things English children take for their lunch. It's not proper food at all. Why do the parents let them? Why don't the schools say something?"

> "In Italy we had 3 course lunches: first pasta, risotto or soup, then either roast beef and potatoes or a ham or cheese omelette with salad or beans, and finishing with fruit or 'budino', a kind of creamy custard. We always had water, too."

New hope here?

What your child eats five days a week at school is important. It can either bolster or undermine the standard at home. In the days of good national guidelines it was not such an issue. Now it seems to be up to parents to get some quality back into the system. However, there are a few rumblings of change.

I know of some schools around the country that have decided to go all out for good food and who have succeeded. In each case it was the determination – sometimes desperation – of the head that produced change, and now the quality of cooking and presentation of their meals is amazing – and can be at the price of free-meal tickets. Each school found it's own solution, but it really shows what can be done. It's up to the head.

ADDRESSES

The Health Education Trust: 18 High Street, Broom, Alcester, Warwicks, B50 4HJ; Fax: 01789 773915; www.healthedtrust.com The trust has detailed advice for parents on a range of issues concerning school food and drink. Its website is very well worth visiting and could answer many of your questions.

Grab 5! has various materials for schools promoting fruit and vegetables and a curriculum pack. Free on the internet: *www.grab5.com* and also, for a small charge, from *Sustain*; tel: 020 7837 1228.

The Food Dudes scheme demonstrated how to get children to eat and enjoy fruit and veg. They are working on getting schools to operate their own schemes. Contact Prof. Fergus Lowe, School of Psychology, University of Wales (Bangor), Brigantia Building, Penrallt Road, Bangor LL57 2AS; tel: 01248 382210; fax: 01248 382599.

The Hyperactive Children's Support Group (HACSG) gives advice on disruptive behaviour caused by food allergies and intolerance. Send a stamped addressed envelope for information. There is also an education pack at £2.50. Write to: HACSG, 71 Whyke Lane, Chichester, West Sussex PO19 7PD; www.hacsg.org.uk

First Milk is a company that installs milk bars in schools: 'First Milk', Elgar Business Centre, Hallow, Worcester WR2 6NJ; tel: 01905 642 300; ask for Dennis Gray.

Milk For Schools is a parent information service on school-based nutrition, including milk and water. Contact Stephanie Spiers at Milk For Schools, PO Box 412, Stafford, Staffs, ST17 9TF; tel: 01785 248 345; www.milkforschools.org.uk

'The Green Machine' can install dispensers of unsweetened, additive-free drinks. Contact the Organic and Natural Food Company Ltd., Unit 10, Denvale Trade Park, 145 Morden Road, Mitcham, Surrey, CF4 4DG; tel: 020 8646 6111.

The **ERIC** campaign provides information on the health benefits of having drinking water available, and has posters and stickers for a small charge. Write to ERIC, 34 Old School House, Britannia Road, Kingswood, Bristol BS15 8DB; tel: 0117 960 3060; email: info@eric.org.uk; www.eric.org.uk

The British Dietetic Association. To find a dietician in your area send them a SAE marked 'Private Practice' 5th Floor, Charles House, 148/9 Great Charles Street, Queensway, Birmingham B3 3HT.

The Parents' Jury. A campaign for parents to join to try and improve the standard of children's food. Contact The Parents Jury, The Food Commission, 94 White Lion Street, London N1 9PF; tel. 020 7837 2250; fax: 020 7837 1141; email: parentsjury@foodcomm.org.uk; www.parentsjury.org

The Food Commission has posters on additives, reading food labels and children's food, suitable for schools. It also campaigns for better food, chiefly through their Food Magazine (£20 p.a. on subscription). Details as for The Parents' Jury above, except for the email address which is: enquiries@foodcomm.org.uk

Do food additives cause hyperactivity and behaviour problems in a geographically defined population of 3-year-olds? (Project TO7004) from The Food Standards Agency Library; tel: 020 7276 8060. There is a summary of the report in issue 59 of the Food Magazine, from The Food Commission above.

Cookware Plus, 18 Winster Park, Lancaster LA1 5 TH; tel: 01524 34111; www.cookwareplus.co.uk; sells the 8.5 litre, stainless steel Demeyere pressure cooker. Expensive, but invaluable!

The Waitrose Cooking Bus goes from school to school, with staff that teach children to cook in the bus's kitchen. Excellent as part of a 'healthy food' project. Interested schools should contact The Royal Society of Arts 'Focus on Food' project at: Design Dimension, Dean Clough, Halifax HX3 5AX; Tel: 01422 383 191.

BOOKS

The Nursery Food Book (2nd edition) by Mary Whiting and Tim Lobstein. A practical book for nursery staff and students on all aspects of food for young children, and with over 50 recipes suitable for any age. £13.99 inc. p&p from The Food Commission.

Managing Nursery Food by Mary Whiting. Advice for nursery managers on providing healthy, tasty food; recipe ideas and sample menus; £9.99 from Nursery World Books: tel: 01454 617370; fax: 01454 618263, quoting ref. ABK14, or visit www.nursery-world.com

The Food our Children Eat (2nd edition) by Joanna Blythman. From weaning a baby to feeding teenagers, relaxed, low-effort strategies that work. £8.99 inc. p&p from The Food Commission.

Fast Food Nation by Eric Schlosser lifts the lid on the fast food industry. Special offer: £7.99 inc. p&p from The Food Commission.

The Vegetable Garden Displayed and **The Fruit Garden Displayed**
Still reputed to be the best guides to growing vegetables and fruit. They go in and out of print over the years and get regularly updated. Usually available in libraries or from The Royal Horticultural Society, 80 Vincent Square, London SW1P 2PE; tel: 010 7834 4333.

The Chips are Down. An excellent guide to planning and promoting healthy eating in schools, and setting up a School Nutrition Action group. £15, including p&p from the Health Education Trust (page 140) or The Food Commission (page 141).

The Robert Carrier Cookbook, pub. Robert Nelson. A brilliant collection of recipes and tips of all kinds, including 50 pages of mouthwatering vegetable recipes. Still available in some libraries.

EPILOGUE

In addition to all these tips and strategies, one very important thing to do is to *complain*! Instead of just feeling angry, seize every opportunity to complain to everyone who promotes unhealthy food and drink to children, from the local fitness centre with its arrays of confectionery to the school with its fast-food dinners. Complain to your local council and your MP. Tell the food manufacturers, too, what you think of their wares.

If enough parents complain enough times, who knows what might be achieved?

RECIPES

T his is a selection of straightforward recipes useful for every day plus recipes for two fresh-fruity birthday cakes, an exceptionally good Christmas pudding and mincemeat! There's also soup that children can make, an excellent pizza, a universally useful tomato sauce, a few tasty ideas for fish, some easy and delicious family dinner dishes, the easiest, juiciest roast chicken.... Other recipe ideas that are simple enough to be described in just a few words may be found under 'Tips' in the chapters on vegetables, fish, fruit and breakfast.

Which flour?

I recommend using what is called 'brown' or '81%' flour, which is semi-wholemeal. It has most of the health benefits of 100% wholemeal flour, but the flakes of bran are much smaller and so it can usually be used like white flour. It is perfect as an all-purpose flour and excellent for baking and making bread.

All the recipes need 'plain' flour.

Abbreviations:

tsp. = teaspoon

tbl. = tablespoon

American equivalents

UK pint = 20 fluid ounces   US pint = 16 fluid ounces

UK tablespoon = $1\frac{1}{2}$ US tablespoons

UK dessertspoon = 1 US tablespoon (approx.)

VEGETABLE SOUP (1)

A delicious but amazingly easy soup that children can help with – or even completely make. It is extremely good. Enough here for a family of four.

$\frac{1}{2}$ kilo (1 lb) potato
2-3 big leeks
4 good sized organic carrots
1 tsp. sugar

salt and black pepper
60g (2 oz) butter
chopped parsley
a little cream

Scrub but do not peel the potatoes and carrots, and cut into small dice.

Split the leeks in half and rinse thoroughly upside down under the cold tap to wash out soil and grit. Cut across into small slices.

Toss the vegetables in a knob of butter to make everything glossy, and cook, stirring, for 2-3 minutes. Pour in $1\frac{1}{2}$ litres ($2\frac{1}{2}$ pints) of water, bring to the boil, then simmer for about half an hour, or until the carrots are completely soft. Mash down well, or put briefly through a food processor. Just before serving, stir in a little cream and scatter on fresh, chopped parsley.

VEGETABLE SOUP (2)

1 bunch asparagus
1 medium onion
1 pint water
smatana or crème fraîche to serve

1 large stalk celery
chicken stock cube
4 cloves garlic

Put all the vegetables except the garlic through the food processor.

Cook with the water and stock cube for 15-20 minutes or until completely cooked.

Liquidize some of it with the (raw) garlic to completely creamy-smooth and stir into the rest. Eat hot with a blob of smatana or crème fraîche.

APRICOT AND CORIANDER SAUCE FOR MACKEREL

1 small mackerel, grilled
1 small onion, finely chopped
a little olive oil

1 tsp. ground coriander
1 tin apricots in syrup
black pepper and salt

Fry the chopped onion very slowly in olive oil to soften but not brown. Stir in the ground coriander, and fry, stirring, for another minute.

Purée the apricots with a little of their syrup, discarding the rest, and add to the onion (yes, this is a very sweet sauce, but it's fabulous, and makes a terrific introduction to mackerel). Add tiny pinches of salt and black pepper, heat through and serve generous amounts of this golden-yellow sauce around the cooked fish. Serve with mashed potato and nothing else.

Variation: Serve mackerel with tomato sauce (see page 158).

FISH CAKES

Allow at least 180g (6 oz) potato and also of fish per teenager. Tinned salmon is fine in this dish.

cooked potato
a little milk
a knob of butter
salt and black pepper

cooked white fish or salmon
chopped fresh parsley
flour
bacon fat or olive oil

Mash the potato with a little hot milk, the butter, black pepper and a tiny pinch of salt. Mix half-and-half with cooked, flaked fish and a little parsley. Shape into a large flat 'cake', coat lightly with flour and fry in bacon fat or olive oil to brown well on both sides, cut into wedges to serve. Or make small individual ones, two or three per person. Eat with bacon and perhaps a good tomato sauce.

HOME MADE FISH FINGERS

180g (6 oz) firm white fish per teenager
flour
beaten egg
fine breadcrumbs
sunflower oil

Have ready some flour mixed with salt and black pepper in a bowl, a bowl of beaten egg and a bowl of home-made breadcrumbs.

Cut any firm white fish into fingers and coat with flour. Then dip each one quickly in a bowl of beaten egg and then into the breadcrumbs. Heat some sunflower oil in a large frying pan and quickly cook the fingers – 2-3 minutes should be enough.

Drain on absorbent paper and serve at once. To keep the oil hot, cook the fingers in batches. Any leftover beaten egg can be cooked as a mini-omelette along with the last fingers!

Variation: Mix a little grated Parmesan cheese into the breadcrumbs.

GRILLED KIPPERS

Buy undyed kippers which, as well as being undyed, are also much less salty and generally milder in flavour. You will see that the kipper's backbone is attached to one fillet. It can easily be removed after grilling. Also meticulously remove all the stray bones in both fillets before serving. Tweezers are useful for this job.

1 undyed kipper between two adults or teenagers
butter or organic 'spreadable' butter
lemon wedges to serve

Pre-heat the grill on full heat. Slash the skin diagonally in two or three places and dot with very little butter. Put under the grill and immediately turn down the heat to less than half. Cook the kipper for one minute. Turn the kipper over and dot with butter. Grill for 7 minutes. Serve with lemon wedges and brown bread and butter.

HERRING FILLETS WITH BUTTER, LEMON AND OATS

Herring is the most nutritious fish of all and the cheapest. Ask the fishmonger to fillet it for you, although it's not hard to do it if you know how. Allow a whole herring (two fillets) per teenager or adult.

1 herring, filleted
1 tbl. rolled oats (not jumbo)
2 tsps. olive oil
a nut of butter

squeeze of lemon juice
salt and black pepper
1 tbl. chopped parsley

First check thoroughly for bones – pull any remaining ones out with tweezers. But ignore the myriad of soft, hair-like bones which are completely harmless. Feel with your fingers for any hard, bony bits along the edges of the fillets and cut them away. Coat the fillets in rolled oats.

Heat the oil in a frying pan and very slowly cook the fillets, skin side first, turning once. They are done when the oats are a pale golden brown. Transfer to a heated plate.

Add the butter, lemon juice, seasoning and parsley to the pan, heat gently to melt the butter, then pour over the fish. Garnish with parsley sprigs and a wedge of lemon for squirting extra juice. Eat at once with mashed potato and a green salad.

KEDGEREE

Enough here for four teenage or adult appetites.

250g (8 oz) rice
120g (4 oz) any white fish (cod,
    coley, whiting etc.)
120g (4 oz) finnan haddock
90 – 120g (3-4 oz) butter
(opt. a little mild, red onion)

2 hard-boiled eggs
2-3 tbls. thick cream
pinch of black pepper
a little chopped parsley
(opt. quartered hard-boiled egg)

First cook the rice (see page 157). When it's done, cover the pan with a folded tea towel and leave so the rice can dry.

Meanwhile, cook the white fish to just done only. (Placed on a plate in a microwave oven, this will take about 2-4 minutes). Break up into flakes with a fork.

Also flake the finnan haddock and gently mix the two fish together.

Chop the eggs and chop the onion very finely if using.

In a good-sized saucepan, melt the butter over a low heat without browning, and then stir in the fish, eggs, onion and black pepper.

Mix the rice in with a fork, and stir over a medium heat until heated through.

Just before serving, stir in the cream. The dish should have a creamy texture. Turn into a hot serving dish and sprinkle with chopped parsley.

Optionally, decorate with pieces of hard-boiled egg.

Golden Kedgeree

ingredients as above
a little oil   1 tsp. turmeric

As above, but colour everything yellow by adding turmeric. In order to stop the turmeric tasting raw and harsh, stir it for a couple of minutes in a drop of oil over medium heat.

When you have done this, melt the butter in the pan over a lowered heat, add the fish, eggs, onion and black pepper as above, and continue with the recipe.

Spotty Yellow Kedgeree

As for Yellow Kedgeree above, but stir in some cooked peas at the last moment.

ROASTED ROOTS (1)

A wonderful way of presenting vegetables of all kinds to children – or anyone. Make up your own favourite combinations:

Carrot and parsnip: Chop into 1 cm dice and toss in olive oil in a shallow baking tray. Roast on the top shelf of hot oven, gas 8, 230C, turning from time to time, for about 30 minutes or until browned and soft.

Mixed vegetables such as red onion, courgettes, aubergine, tomatoes, red or yellow peppers. Chop roughly into 2.5 cm (1 inch) dice, toss in olive oil in a shallow baking tray.

Roast on the top shelf of the oven at gas 9, 240C, for 30-40 minutes, or until soft and slightly browned. (Peel the tomatoes beforehand if you wish – see page 47)

ROASTED ROOTS (2)

Vegetables that look and taste as good as this are hard to refuse. If you double the recipe there'll be some to reheat the next day. Quantities here feed 2 hungry teenagers and two adults.

250g (8 oz) organic carrots	250g (8 oz) parsnips
250g (8 oz) celeriac	250g (8 oz) red onions
250g (8 oz) swede	115g (4 oz) tiny potatoes
3 tbls. goose fat or olive oil	salt and black pepper

Heat some water in a large saucepan while you prepare the vegetables: scrub the potatoes and carrots, peel and quarter the onions and peel the other vegetables. Cut the carrots, parsnips, celeriac and swede into chunks the size of the potatoes.

Heat the oven to gas 6, 200C, and have ready a large baking tray with the goose fat or olive oil in.

When the water is boiling, throw in all the vegetables, bring back to the boil and cook for 5-7 minutes. Drain well on thick newspaper. Rough up the surface of the potatoes with a fork for a crispy texture.

Put the baking tray in the oven to heat the fat. When it's hot – in about a minute (the goose fat will smoke when its ready, the olive oil shouldn't) – tip in the vegetables, turn them quickly to coat all over, then roast for 30-40 minutes turning once. They're done when nicely caramelized and when a skewer slides easily through the thickest chunks.

SWISS CHARD

It looks like deep green, glossy spinach and has thick creamy-white stalks, but its taste is milder and easier for children to like.

Cut off the stalks and cook them separately: Slice them across diagonally (call them 'diamonds') and simmer in a little water, then toss in butter – or let children dip the stalks in melted butter and eat as finger food. Simmer the leaves separately, toss in butter and serve as you would any other green vegetable.

KABOCHA PUMPKIN

Cut the peeled and seeded pumpkin into 2-3cm dice and steam for about five minutes. Toss in butter and serve. They taste somewhat like chestnuts.

Alternatively cut into 5cm (2 inch) chunks and roast in hot fat at gas 6, 200C for 40-50 minutes turning once.

CARROT AND SWEDE CRUSH

Boil diced carrot and chunks of swede together until just soft, using a little more carrot than swede. Roughly mash them together. Beat in butter, a pinch of salt and plenty of black pepper.

CHESTNUTS - HOW TO PREPARE AND COOK

Getting chestnuts out of their shells in one piece need not be difficult, but success depends on several things: having really fresh chestnuts, working quickly and keeping them hot and wet throughout, and making sure you get the inner membrane off along with the shell. Here's a good method:

Put each chestnut flat side down onto a chopping board and with a sharp knife slice off its tip, taking off a tiny bit of the nut. Then throw the nuts into a saucepan of boiling water, making sure the water completely covers them. Bring back to the boil then simmer for seven minutes. Remove from the heat. Alternatively microwave them for 2 minutes on High, then wait 1 minute to loosen the shells. Or just freeze them.

Remove one chestnut from the water at a time, and stand it on its end, tip uppermost. Working quickly, slide the point of the knife down the flat side of the nut, between the nut and the inner membrane, pushing membrane and shell off together. Make sure you cut right across to both left and right of the side of the nut. Then push the knife down further so it goes under the hard base. With luck, the chestnut will come out cleanly, but if it doesn't, work the knife around the sides. If it's stubborn, return it to the hot water and try again later.

Discard any discoloured bits of nut and, of course, any black ones – there are usually a few in each batch. Simmer the chestnuts in chicken stock for about 20 minutes or until they are cooked through. Serve mixed with Brussels sprouts or alongside red cabbage or as a winter garnish to poultry. Of course you can also roast them in the fire for the best flavour of all.

CAULIFLOWER AND BROCCOLI CHEESE

You'll never want ordinary cauliflower cheese again! Vary the proportions of the vegetables to suit your own family's taste.

cheese sauce (page 158)
cauliflower and broccoli florets
pan fried potatoes to serve

a few cherry tomatoes
2-3 slices unsmoked bacon

Steam or boil the florets until a knife will slide smoothly into the thickest part of the stalk. Arrange in a heated serving dish. While they are cooking, fry the bacon in a shallow pan, drain and crumble. Set aside.

Then roll a few cherry tomatoes in the same pan to warm them through. If they burst, no matter. Scrape up all the pan juices and add to the cheese sauce.

Scatter the tomatoes and bacon pieces over the vegetables and cover the whole thing very generously with cheese sauce.

Variation: top with grated cheese mixed with a few breadcrumbs and grill briefly to golden brown. The breadcrumbs will become crispy and well browned.

PAN FRIED POTATOES

boiled potatoes
goose fat, olive oil or bacon fat

This is quick to do if you have some potatoes ready cooked from the previous day. Waxy ones are best. Make sure they are quite dry and then cut them into chunks. Toss and fry quickly over medium-high heat in a little fat to brown on all sides. Drain on absorbent paper. Tastier than chips and, if the chunks are a good size, less fatty.

BUBBLE AND SQUEAK

Traditional favourite! Allow at least 180g (6 oz) of potato and of greens per teenager.

cooked potato
Brussels sprouts or cabbage
a little hot milk
a knob of butter
salt and black pepper
flour for coating
bacon fat or olive oil

Mash the cooked potato with a little hot milk, a knob of butter, black pepper and a tiny pinch of salt.

Mix half-and-half with cooked, roughly mashed Brussels sprouts or finely chopped, cooked cabbage.

Shape into a large flat 'cake', coat lightly with flour, and fry in bacon fat or olive oil to brown well on both sides. Cut into wedges to serve.
Or make small individual ones, two or three per person. Eat with bacon or ham, and perhaps a good tomato sauce.

Tip on boiling vegetables

There is never any need to salt the cooking water when boiling (or steaming) vegetables. It makes little difference to the taste, and in any case children need to be guided away from acquiring a taste for salt.

Vegetable cooking water which has not been salted is nutritious and can be used for further cooking. But don't re-use the water from cooking brassicas (cabbage, broccoli, sprouts) as it could have thyroid-damaging properties.

HOW TO COOK BROWN RICE

So easy to cook – it doesn't stick or go gluey like white rice, and it's great for fibre and B vitamins. Allow 2 oz for an adult or teenager. Measure the water by *volume*:

115g (4 oz) rice needs 430ml (15 fl oz) water
225g (8 oz) rice needs 560ml (1 pint) of water
340g (12 oz) rice needs 700ml (24 fl oz) water

First wash the rice in a sieve under the cold tap for a few seconds, then drain well.

Throw into fast-boiling water in a medium-sized saucepan, bring back to the boil and skim.

Then, turn the heat down as low as it will go. Cover the pan. Barely simmer without stirring:

Short-grain (round or 'pudding') rice needs 25 minutes, long-grain rice needs 30 minutes, very thin grains such as Basmati rice need only about 12 minutes

When the rice is cooked, it will have absorbed all its cooking water. If a little water is left, leave the rice for a few minutes to finish absorbing it.

No need to salt the water, but a bay leaf adds flavour. Either serve at once, or keep warm for up to half an hour or so in a loosely covered dish in the oven.

TOMATO SAUCE

1 medium-large onion	big pinches of thyme & sage
1 large tin tomatoes	small pinch salt & black pepper
1 bay leaf	dash of ketchup
olive oil	tiny pinch cayenne pepper

Over a very low heat, cook the finely chopped onion with the bay leaf in the oil to soften but not brown. Add a little water (or juice from the tin) from time to time to stop it catching. Then add everything else.

Mash down and cook, stirring often, to a thickened sauce. Enough for one large pizza; also excellent with white fish, mackerel, chicken and pork. Try it on toast as a snack or mixed with baked beans.

CHEESE SAUCE

The secret of this sauce is the onion and also the added flavourings

1 small onion, finely chopped	50-60g (2oz) grated Cheddar
a little sunflower oil	tiny pinch salt & black pepper
a bay leaf	few drops Worcester sauce
300ml ($\frac{1}{2}$ pint) milk	tiny pinch mustard
60g (2 oz) butter	
60g (2 oz) flour	*a hand-whisk*

In a small saucepan, cook the onion in the oil with the bay leaf over a very low heat to soften but not brown. Add a little water from time to time to stop it catching.

When it's quite soft, tip in the milk, butter and flour all at once and whisk over medium heat to a thickened sauce. Add everything else. Then stir over a low heat for 2 minutes to cook the flour thoroughly.

Tip: If you make this sauce in advance, carefully cover the top of the sauce with milk to stop a skin forming.

Variations on cheese sauce:

Mushroom sauce: omit the cheese and add pan-fried sliced mushrooms. Fry them quickly over high heat in a speck of butter and lemon juice, a few seconds only. They should be browned but not soft.

Parsley sauce: omit the cheese, and add a heaped tablespoon of chopped, fresh parsley.

PASTA SAUCE A LA BOLOGNESE

A deliciously brilliant way of completely disguising liver! Enough here for two hearty teenage appetites.

1 carton (227g) chicken livers	2 tsps. whole wheat flour
2 cloves garlic	good pinch thyme, sage, basil
50 -100g (2 - 3 oz) mushrooms	2 tbl. olive oil
1 tbl. tomato ketchup	tiny pinch salt & black pepper
1 good-sized onion, chopped	600ml (1 pint) chicken stock

In a small saucepan, soften the onion and garlic in the oil without browning, for about 10 minutes. If necessary add a little water to stop it catching. Wipe and slice the mushrooms.

Roughly chop rhe livers and toss them in the flour. Add them to saucepan when the onions have cooked for 10 minutes and toss over medium heat to brown very slightly.

Pour in the stock and the other ingredients except the mushrooms, bring to the boil, then lower the heat to a simmer and cook slowly, uncovered to a thickened sauce, mashing down as the livers cook. After 10 minutes add the mushrooms. Stir from time to time to prevent it catching.

ROAST DRUMSTICKS

Eat as finger food as a meaty treat. Roast in a chicken brick as opposite, or in a covered tray. Cook as many drumsticks as you like and freeze most of them for later.

chicken drumsticks
sliced onion
a few very thin slices of carrot
black pepper and a little salt
thyme and parsley

Fill a shallow baking dish with as many drumsticks as it will hold in a single layer, tucking the other ingredients underneath the meat. Cover with foil.

Depending on the size of the drumsticks and on how tightly you have packed them together, cook at gas 4, 180C, on the centre shelf for about an hour. When they are done, a skewer pushed into the thickest part will produce clear, not pink, juices, and the meat will be very loose on the bone.

Drink the strained juices as chicken soup – and a child may enjoy eating the luscious cooking vegetables as finger food.

Alternatively, you could make your own 'nuggets' with pieces of chicken (leg meat has the most flavour) dipped in egg and breadcrumbs and quickly fried in a speck of oil.

CHICKEN-BRICK ROAST

Use a terracotta 'chicken brick' for the easiest, most problem free and luscious roast chicken of all. You will never want to roast a chicken any other way! You simply put the chicken in the brick, put on the cover and cook it. The chicken will be golden brown, moist and tender – and the brick will contain delicious chicken gravy. No basting, no turning...no worry. Put a few flavourings inside the chicken and underneath it for the best flavour.

1 roasting chicken no bigger than 2 kilos (4$\frac{1}{4}$ lbs)
1 sliced onion
1 small thinly sliced carrot
a little salt and pepper
thyme and parsley

Put the vegetables, herbs and seasoning inside and under the chicken in the brick and put on the cover. Put into *an unheated oven* – or the brick could crack. A 2 kilo chicken will feed 6 adults or teenagers and will take about 2 hours to cook at gas 4, 180C. But it's even nicer to leave it for almost twice that time at gas 2, 150C, and it will shrink less. It's done when the legs are very loose, or when a skewer inserted into the thickest part of the thigh produces clear (not pink) juices.

• This is also a delicious and easy way of cooking small 'roasts' of beef, lamb or pork, and also of smaller birds such as guinea fowl or quail. Look out for these more unusual birds at bargain prices in supermarkets just before their sell-by date.

• As a treat, children can enjoy having their 'own' small bird, and, eating it as finger food, can make a good job of picking every scrap of meat off the bones!

WOLF STEW

Another good way of presenting liver without saying what it is. The liver is cut up into various shapes – triangles, strips, so children can guess which bit of the wolf they are eating! This recipe is enough for two teenagers or adults.

250g (8 oz) lambs or organic pork liver sliced thinly

1 heaped tbl. whole wheat flour	1 heaped tsp. paprika
1 medium-sized onion, sliced thinly	150ml ($^1/_4$ pint) chicken stock
2 tbls. olive oil	250g (8oz) tin tomatoes
30g (1 oz) butter	pinch of thyme and sage
1 red pepper, sliced	salt and black pepper

Heat the oil and half the butter in a medium-sized saucepan or sauté pan. Toss the liver in the flour. Fry over medium heat in the oil-and-butter for one minute, turning once, then remove to a plate.

Cook the sliced onion in the pan over low heat, covered for 5 minutes. Add the red pepper and cook for a further 5 minutes. Shake the pan from time to time to prevent sticking, and add a little water if necessary.

Meanwhile, use scissors to cut the liver into various shapes.

Melt the remaining butter in the pan, dust in any remaining flour with the paprika. Stir round for a minute to cook the flour and brown it a little.

Tip in the tomatoes and the stock, and seasoning. Stir in, scraping the pan as you do so, and bring to the boil. Then replace the liver, add the herbs, and cook over a very low heat for a couple of minutes until the liver is *just* cooked through. The middle should just have stopped being pink. Never overcook liver – it's one of the few meats that gets tougher the longer you cook it. If in doubt, snip a piece in half to check the colour inside.

Serve with plenty of potatoes mashed with butter and hot milk plus peas or ratatouille.

Variations on Wolf Stew

• Add green, orange or yellow peppers, cooked carrot or parsnip pieces, tinned sweetcorn...or whatever you think your children might find amusing in a wolf stew!

• Slice lambs' kidneys thinly and use instead of liver – or mix the two.

• Use mustard instead of paprika. Stir wholegrain mustard in at the end.

BABY MEATBALLS

WITH YOGHURT-DILL SAUCE

Enough for 2 teenagers or adults

250g (8 oz) best minced beef
1-2 tsps. dill weed
salt and black pepper
1 tbl. olive oil
30g (1 oz) butter
300ml ($\frac{1}{2}$ a pint) creamy yoghurt

In a bowl, mix the beef with a pinch of the dill, a very little salt and pepper and about half a teaspoon of the yoghurt. Shape into 12 tiny meatballs. If you have time, chill them for half an hour to firm them.

Heat the oil in a frying pan and roll the meatballs in it until just cooked through.

Remove to warmed plates. Melt the butter in the pan, add the rest of the dill and a pinch of salt and pepper. Then, over a very low heat, stir in the yoghurt. It may curdle, but it doesn't much matter! Pour the sauce over the meatballs and eat at once with mashed potatoes and a green salad.

MEATY RICE STUFFING FOR VEGETABLES

This delicious stuffing is enough for two adult or teenage appetites. Use it for stuffing red peppers, aubergine, courgettes, marrow. Vegetarians could substitute cooked aduki beans for the meat.

50g (2 oz) brown rice, cooked (see page 157)
a bay leaf
115g (4 oz) lean minced beef or lamb
1 good sized onion, chopped
olive oil for frying
pinches of sage and thyme
salt and black pepper
splash of tomato ketchup

Fry the chopped onion with the bay leaf in the olive oil in a good-sized frying pan until softened but not browned. Add a little water from time to time to prevent it sticking. When it's cooked tip onto a plate.

Meanwhile prepare the vegetables: halve and deseed the peppers; gouge out other types, chop up what you have taken out, discarding any large seeds, and add to the onions. When it's all thoroughly cooked, tip out into a bowl. Remove the bay leaf.

Mix a little salt and pepper into the meat and press down into the frying pan. Cook over a fairly high heat to brown. Turn over and brown the other side. Check that the meat is cooked through and that there are no pink bits. Then crumble up and mix in the onion.

Mix in the cooked rice, and add the ketchup and herbs.

To assemble the finished dish:
Steam the vegetables *upside down* so they don't get waterlogged, until done (aubergines must be very well done). Pack with the stuffing on a serving dish, mounding it up well. Cover generously with cheese sauce and serve immediately. Or cover with grated cheese and grill.

THE BEST BURGERS

If your children are used to these they may well reject commercial ones!
Quantities for one good-sized burger:

115g (4 oz) best minced beef
half a very small onion
dash of Worcester sauce
black pepper and a little salt
sunflower oil

Chop the onion very finely and evenly. Fry it in a little sunflower oil until
completely soft but not browned. To stop it catching, keep adding a little
water.

Mix with the other ingredients, shape, and fry, preferably in a ridged pan,
in a little sunflower oil over medium heat, turning once. Each side should
be well-browned and the middle just done, with no pink bits.

Eat with any trimmings the children like – shredded lettuce, tomato
slices, spring onions, gherkins, mustard, ketchup, pickle. Either have it
as a knife-and-fork meal with jacket potatoes or sauté potatoes or oven
chips (or with big chip-shop chips if there is a fish shop nearby), or as
finger food inside a whole wheat bun. Put a little strong-flavoured grated
cheese in the bun if your children like that.

LAMB NÎMOISE

A perfect one-pot dish that needs a long, slow cook.

3 slices from a leg of lamb, no more than 1 cm thick,
and weighing a good kilo (2 lbs) altogether
4 rashers streaky bacon, cut into strips
2-3 cloves garlic, sliced thinly
2 tbls. olive oil
4 small-medium potatoes, scrubbed, cubed
a piece of fennel cut into quarters
a small aubergine, cubed
3-4 ripe tomatoes, quartered
3-4 carrots, sliced thickly and diagonally
2 small onions, sliced thickly
thyme
salt and fresh black pepper

a fireproof dish 2.5 litres (4 $\frac{1}{2}$ pints) capacity or a casserole dish and a frying pan

Check the meat for splinters of bone, and remove excess fat.

Heat the oil in your dish, then drop in half the bacon strips, cover with the meat, and poke the garlic slices down between the pieces of meat. Cover with the rest of the bacon. Sprinkle on a little salt, pepper and thyme.

Pile on the prepared vegetables, with a little more seasoning and thyme between the layers.

Put into a hot oven, gas 6, 200C, for about 20 minutes, then lower the heat to gas 2-3, 155-165C, cover tightly and leave for 3 $\frac{1}{2}$ to 4 hours. It will smell heavenly and, miraculously, there should be a quantity of juice in the dish from the meat and vegetables (but check once or twice and add a little water if there isn't). You should be able to cut the meat with a spoon.

STEAK AND KIDNEY STEW

An excellent cook-ahead dish. Be generous with the kidney which is extremely nutritious as well as giving the dish extra hearty flavour. This recipe makes a large amount, so freeze some for a 'ready meal' later.

1 kilo (2lb) braising steak
$\frac{1}{2}$ kilo (1 lb) ox or pork kidney
300g (10 oz) onion
wholemeal flour

beef stock or water
sage, thyme and parsley
salt and black pepper

Cut the steak (or ask the butcher to) into half-inch dice. Cut away the white core of the kidney and discard, then chop the kidney into roughly the same size pieces. Coat all the meat with the flour by tossing in a plastic bag with the salt, pepper and herbs. Slice the onions.

Put the meat mixture into a casserole dish, scattering the onion slices between the layers. Add enough stock (a stock cube is fine) or water to almost cover. Put on the lid.

Cook at gas 4 (180C) for 2 $\frac{1}{2}$ to 3 hours or until the beef can be cut with a metal spoon. (Meat cut into 2.5cm (1 inch) cubes will take 4 hours.) Serve with carrots and a green vegetable.

Variation: Add mushrooms. Wipe about 220g (8 oz) mushrooms with a damp cloth, slice each mushroom into three, then toss in two batches over high heat in a nut of butter until browned well. Add to the casserole just before the end.

Steak and kidney pie

Fill a pie dish with the cold cooked meat mixture. Cover with pastry (as on page 176), with a pie funnel or upturned egg cup in the centre of the dish to help support the pastry.

Bake at gas 6-7, 205C, for 20 minutes, then loosely cover the pastry with foil and cook for a further 15 minutes at gas 5, 190C.

TREASURE-TROVE DINNER

Or call it 'Mystery-pot dinner' – or anything else. This is an endlessly variable, dead easy, one-pot dinner dish of meat and vegetables which you can throw together in no time. Two tips: repeat favourite combinations but don't let it get too predictable; and always put in lots of onion to give it a base of good flavour.

Basic ingredients:
Beef, lamb or pork cut into 1.5cm dice, or chicken legs left whole, allowing 120g (4oz) meat, *or* a half chicken leg per adult or teenager; at least 1 onion, roughly sliced per adult or teenager, flour mixed with black pepper and a little salt, mixed vegetables, as below, pinches of thyme, sage and parsley, stock or water.

Add any of the following: celery stalks cut into thirds, potatoes in big chunks, swede and squash cut into quarters, whole small turnips, whole carrots, tomatoes (tinned or fresh), aubergine in big chunks, quartered fennel, whole garlic cloves, the white part of leeks, whole 'pickling' onions, tomato purée, unsmoked streaky bacon rashers cut into large pieces, butter beans, split peas and lentils.

Haricot or flageolet beans can be added but must be soaked in cold water for about 12 hours first and rinsed well. Red beans should not be used with this method because of their inherent toxins.

You can also change the flavour by adding things such as soy sauce or curry spices. You can replace some of the water with red or white wine – don't worry, all the alcohol will be destroyed in the long cooking!

Ingredients to stir in at the end include: cooked peas; cooked pasta pieces; ham in strips or dice; sliced, quickly fried mushrooms; sliced, cooked cabbage, chopped fresh herbs; grated cheese, crème fraîche, yoghurt, grain mustard.

Toss the meat in a plastic bag with the seasoned flour to coat well.

Put into a large casserole dish in layers with at least three vegetables and the herbs.

Almost cover with stock or water. Cover tightly. Cook for about 2 hours at gas 4, 180C.

• *Busy parents tip*: Assemble this dish in the evening before the day you want to eat it and put in the fridge. Next morning, simply put the dish in the oven and slow cook it all day for a 'ready meal' that evening.

However, as the oven temperature is very low, it would be safest to use this method only for beef and lamb. With this method, set your oven as low as it will go and cook the casserole for at least eight hours. Start it at breakfast time for your evening meal. Ovens vary however, so have a test run.

PIZZA

This is an especially good recipe. Make up the dough in bulk and freeze it in separate portions, ready to use. Plenty for two hungry teenagers.

150g (5oz) plain flour
60ml (2 fl.oz) sunflower oil
1 ball Mozzarella
40-50g (2oz) Parmesan,
    freshly grated

60ml (2 fl.oz) milk
15g (½ oz) fresh yeast *or*
    10g (¼ oz) dried
tomato sauce as on page 158

toppings:
sliced mushrooms, salami, shredded ham, sardines, anchovies, black olives sliced, tomato sauce (page 158), peppers, chopped parsley, etc.

First make the base: heat the milk to just tepid and pour onto the yeast in a small bowl. Add the oil, stir and leave in a warm place for 10 minutes. Then add the flour and mix to a very soft, moist, pliable dough. Add more liquid if the dough seems at all dry or stiff. Knead in your hands for 3 minutes. Put it to rise to double its size in the bowl, covered with a plate, in a warm place.

Meanwhile slice the Mozzarella roughly and prepare the toppings as necessary.

Punch down the risen dough and roll out thinly on a floured surface to fit your pizza tray. Heat the oven to gas 7, 210C.

Pinch up the edge all round. Spread the warm tomato sauce onto the base, scatter the Mozzarella pieces over the sauce along with the other toppings and dust with Parmesan.

Bake for 10 minutes in the upper part of the oven. Let cool for 5-10 minutes to set the cheese.

These quantities will make a round pizza 30cm (1 ft) in diameter, or fill a baking sheet, roughly 25cm by 35cm (10 by 14 inches)

SANDWICH IDEAS

Children can enjoy making their own sandwiches especially if they have some say in the choice of fillings. Open sandwiches can be fun to make: you can see exactly what you're getting and be a bit artistic arranging the 'filling'. Toasted sandwiches make a good cold weather treat. Using different kinds of bread as well as a variety of fillings keeps it all interesting, as does discovering good combinations of ingredients. For example, tomato and avocado slices are great in a sandwich with curd cheese and with sunflower seeds to add crunch; ham with cheese and pineapple makes a delicious sandwich, and especially good when toasted; strong Cheddar is good with honey.

A few ideas for components:

Bread: Whole wheat, Granary, Greek bread, pitta, baps, nan, bagels, rolls, fruit buns, fruit bread, crispbreads, Pumpernickel, rye, sourdough, tortilla wraps.

Proteins: hard cheeses (Cheddar, Cheshire, red Leicester, Gruyere), curd cheese, cream cheese, hard boiled egg, scrambled egg, tuna, sardines, salmon, prawns, crab, chicken, ham, salami, sliced sausage, haslet, tongue, peanut butter, almond butter, tahini, hummus. For children over five, sunflower, sesame or pumpkin seeds could be added for a crunchy texture.

Moisteners: thin slices of cucumber, celery, radish, avocado, tomato (nicer if peeled), apple, gherkin, pineapple; thin sticks of celeriac, carrot, yellow and red pepper; big tufts of cress, chopped watercress, shredded lettuce, chopped chives, sliced grapes or banana, sultanas, fruit puree, honey, chutney.

SWEET THINGS

CRUNCHY GRANOLA

An exceptionally delicious breakfast cereal. I think it would tempt almost anyone! Also useful as a dessert topping, but keep it crisp by adding it at the last moment.

The ingredients and quantities are both variable – adjust them to the size of your baking tray and what you have in the store cupboard.

350g ($^3/_4$lb) rolled oats
1 handful wheatgerm
2 handfuls nuts (peanuts, Brazils, almonds, etc)
30-60g (1-2 oz) sunflower seeds
30-60g (1-2 oz) green pumpkin seeds
30-60g (1-2 oz) sesame seeds
1-2 tbls. sunflower oil
1-2 tbls. clear honey

Chop the nuts roughly. Mix all the nuts and seeds together.

Put the oil and honey in a small saucepan and heat just enough to make the honey pourable. Stir this into the nuts and seeds.

Spread out in a shallow baking tray. Roast at gas 4, 180C, turning once or twice, until the mixture is lightly browned – about half and hour.

When completely cold, tip into an air-tight container to keep crisp.

Eat with milk. Good with summer red fruits or banana.

MILK SHAKES

These can almost be a meal in themselves. Serve at breakfast – even *as* breakfast in an emergency, and also as a pick-me-up or an ultra quick snack during the day. They can be thin, with just milk and a flavouring, or thickened with powdered milk and hard-boiled egg (the old idea of beating raw egg into milk has gone – unfortunately so because the cooked egg leaves a slight taste, although this does disappear after a day. A dash of Cointreau masks the boiled-egg-taste, but that of course is for adult versions!).

Vanilla
Simply stir in a few drops of vanilla extract – try to get the real thing, not just the chemical food flavouring, although the taste is much the same.

Strawberry 1
Liquidize some fresh strawberries (or slightly thawed frozen ones) in the milk with a tiny pinch of sugar.

Strawberry 2
Liquidize about half a teaspoon of good strawberry jam with a small cupful of milk. Surprisingly, perhaps, this is enough to turn the milk pale pink and have a strawberry-ish flavour.

Raspberry, blackberry, cherry or blueberry
As for strawberry, with stronger flavour and more colour, particularly in the case of blackberry. The only sensible way of stoning cherries is to use a cherry stoner. Get a strong, metal one, which will shoot the stones out in no time – a great job for children, but possibly best done out of doors on lots of newspaper...

Apricot
As for strawberry, although the taste is intensified by adding dried apricots or a very little apricot jam as well as fresh apricots.

PICK-ME-UP SHAKE

A substantial shake – almost a meal.

300ml ($^1/_2$ pint) fresh orange juice
1-2 hard-boiled eggs
1-2 tsps. brewers' yeast
teacup of plain yoghurt
3 heaped tbls. powdered milk
1 large banana
a grating of nutmeg
2-3 drops vanilla extract
300ml ($^1/_2$ pint) milk
other fruit to taste

Into a liquidiser (not a food processor), pour most of the orange juice, and leaving the machine running, add all the other ingredients, adding the milk and the remaining juice last. Taste, and add other soft fruits if you wish. You could add a whole carton of frozen orange juice. Store in the fridge for up to three days.

FRUIT PYRAMIDS

Pile satsumas, for example, into a big pyramid (actually more of a cone shape) on a large, fairly flat plate. It looks extra good if you can tuck a ring of dark green leaves under the fruit, and perhaps push a leaf or two between the fruits, here and there. Bay leaves are good for this.

Clementines, peaches, nectarines and small red apples all lend themselves well to this idea. When you buy clementines, pick those with green leaves attached – or pick up a few loose ones – to use in the arrangement. Make a mixed-fruit pyramid – satsumas/clementines and red apples look good.

Of course, wash the fruit beforehand and dry it so it looks shiny and inviting.

PINEAPPLE ON A PLATE

A nice way of serving a pineapple as a dessert and making it into a treat. Choose a ripe fruit with a good looking top. Look out for pineapples labelled as 'extra sweet'– they really are extra sweet.

Slice off the green leaves with a little of the pineapple attached, and stand it in the centre of a serving plate.

Cut off the base and discard. Cut off the peel in thick strips, and then cut the flesh into rounds. You could remove the centres with an apple corer but it's not essential.

Arrange the slices around the leaves, overlapping them if necessary.

Eat with a spoon and fork. (Adults may like to pour on a little Cointreau...)

WINTER FRUIT SALAD

This tangy-and-sweet fruit salad is useful when the summer fruit is over. Eat with smatana or crème fraîche, or just on its own. Enough here for a family of four.

2 oranges
2 red grapefruit
1 apple
a few seedless grapes
1-2 bananas

Chop up the citrus fruit, then the apple and mix together. Add the grapes. Just before serving, slice the banana and add. You could add kiwi fruit too, or satsuma segments, or slices of ripe pear perhaps instead of the grapes.

SHORTCRUST PASTRY

This is a real melt-in-the-mouth pastry, excellent for both sweet and savoury dishes. It's also easier than most pastry recipes to handle and roll out thinly, and easier still if it's made the day before.

Children could try rolling this and making decorations for pies!

60g (2 oz) butter
175g (6 oz) plain flour
6 tsps. ice cold water

60g (2 oz) lard
pinch salt

Sift the flour with the salt into a mixing bowl.

Have the fat rather cold. Cut it into the flour with two blunt knives, criss-crossing them against each other until the fat is reduced to small pieces. Then finish off by quickly rubbing the fat into the flour with your finger tips until the mixture looks likes like coarse breadcrumbs – a few seconds only. Don't over rub! The mixture must not get sticky.

Cut in the water. Firmly press the dough into a ball using one hand while the other hand holds the bowl. Knead smooth for a few seconds only, wrap or cover and chill for at least half an hour to 'rest' it.

When you're ready to use it, re-knead for a few seconds, then roll out gently and evenly on a lightly floured surface with a floured rolling pin. Keep checking for bits of fat on the surface, and also on the pin, that could make the pastry stick: keep rubbing both with floury fingers.

After every few rolls, move the pastry onto a dusting of fresh flour, but don't try to turn it over – the table rolls the underneath. To lift it, flip it over the rolling pin.

• You can make pastry perfectly in the food processor, but follow the same general rules. Don't over-process or you'll have a sticky mass, impossible to roll out.

• For pastry that's especially easy to roll out, make it the day before and chill it, wrapped in (non PVC) cling film, overnight. If the pastry cracks as you roll it, just gather it together, re-knead for a few seconds and re-roll.

REAL CUSTARD

If possible, use vanilla sugar (made by storing a split vanilla pod in a jar of sugar). Otherwise, use a good vanilla extract. The cornflour helps prevent the custard curdling.

2 eggs yolks	300ml ($\frac{1}{2}$ pint) milk
3 heaped tsps. vanilla sugar	pinch salt
1 tsp. cornflour mixed into 2 tsps. water	

Beat the yolks and sugar well, then mix in the cornflour. Boil the milk in a small heavy saucepan, and gradually whisk into the eggs. Return to the pan and stir over a *very low* heat to a thickened custard. Add a tiny pinch of salt.

To wash strawberries:
Place them in a sieve or colander and wash briefly under the cold tap. Then roll gently on absorbent paper (clean newspaper is fine) until they are dry. Then hull them. Transfer to a plate, preferably in a single layer, and chill until needed.

To peel peaches:
Place in hot (not boiling) water for 10 seconds or so. Remove, put into cold water to set the skin, then peel and use. Don't peel peaches in advance of using them or they will go brown.

FRUIT JELLY

A brilliant party recipe – but use the general idea for any time. The version here is put into a loaf tin and then turned out, but any mould will do – and you can just as easily use a glass trifle bowl so the layers of fruit can be seen.

3 ripe bananas
3 kiwi fruit
half a pink melon
box of raspberries
3 large navel oranges
300ml ($\frac{1}{2}$ pint) fresh orange juice
20g ($\frac{1}{2}$ oz) powdered gelatine – or use gelatine leaves

an 800g (2 lb) loaf tin lightly oiled

Peel and thinly slice the kiwi fruit and line the bottom of the tin in an even layer.

Cut each banana into three lengthways slices and lay on the kiwis. Cover the bananas with a layer of raspberries. Peel the melon, slice thinly and arrange neatly on the raspberries.

Segment the oranges. Arrange on top in a final layer, saving any juice.

Heat half the orange juice, sprinkle the gelatine powder onto it in an even layer and stir in to dissolve. If any grains refuse to dissolve, then heat the juice very gently and stir until they do. Don't let the gelatine boil or it will go stringy. If using leaves follow the instructions on the packet.

Then, tip in the rest of the (cold) juice, and pour it over the fruit. Chill to set.

To serve: run a knife carefully around the sides of the tin, wipe the bottom of the tin with a dishcloth wrung out in hot water, and turn out.

CHOCOLATE AND HAZELNUT CAKE

No flour in this super chocolate cake – just ground hazelnuts. Fill with lots of fresh fruit and a little cream as a birthday or party cake.

for the cake:

140g (5 oz) hazelnuts
140g (5 oz caster sugar)
4 eggs
100g ($3\frac{1}{2}$ oz) plain chocolate

to finish:

150ml ($\frac{1}{4}$ pint) thick cream, whipped
any fresh soft fruit such as raspberries and strawberries
two 15cm (6-inch) diameter sandwich cake tins

First grease the tins, line each with a disc of oiled greaseproof paper and dust with flour.

Toast the nuts, rub off their skins in a tea towel and then pulverise.

Whisk the sugar and eggs with an electric beater until thick and mousse-like.

Break up the chocolate and melt it with a teaspoon or so of water in a bowl over boiling water. Beat a little into the egg mixture, then fold in the rest along with the nuts.

Divide the mixture between the two tins and bake side by side at gas 4, 180C for 40 minutes or until springy to the touch. Turn out and cool.

When cold, sandwich together with whipped cream and lots of fresh fruit. Spread more cream on the top and decorate with fruit.

MIDSUMMER BIRTHDAY CAKE

This is perfect for filling with masses of fresh fruit and looks – and tastes – spectacular. You must have a proper *moule a manqué* cake tin though (it has sloping sides) for the real effect. Buy a '3-egg' size, which holds 3 pints (roughly 1.8 litres).

3 eggs	2 level tsps. baking powder
280g (10 oz) caster sugar	100ml ($3\frac{1}{2}$ fl oz) water
200g (7 oz) plain flour	pinch salt

Filling:

300ml ($\frac{1}{2}$ pint) double cream (or mix with a little thick yoghurt)
the juice of an orange
2 big boxes of strawberries
3 ripe peaches or nectarines
sprigs of red-currants, or more strawberries

Grease the tin, line the bottom with a circle of greaseproof paper (butter wrapper is fine), then grease the paper. Shake a little sieved flour into the tin, then tip out the surplus.

Have a shelf half way down the oven and pre-heat at gas 4-5, 185C.

Sieve the flour with the salt and baking powder.

Whisk the eggs and sugar together with an electric beater in a large bowl until the mixture is thick and mousse-like and almost white.

Using a metal spoon, carefully fold in the water and flour. Don't over-fold or you'll lose volume. Pour into the prepared tin.

Bake for about 40 minutes until a light golden brown and set. To test, push the top of the cake with your finger: if a dent remains, the cake isn't done. The ultimate test is to see if the cake has shrunk away from the sides of the tin.

Let the cake half cool in the tin, then loosen all the way round with a blunt knife, tap the tin sideways in case of a sideways air-lock and tip the cake out carefully onto a wire rack. Leave to cool completely.

To fill, first save about ten of the best-looking strawberries for the top. Slice the rest and put them into a bowl with the orange juice. Skin the peaches (no need to peel nectarines), slice them into the bowl and leave to macerate for at least 15 minutes.

Meanwhile, split the cake open and place the bottom half on a thick silver board or a large, flat serving plate. Whip the cream to *almost* stiff and mix in the yoghurt if using.

Cover the bottom layer of cake with slightly less than half the cream and then the fruit mixture, including all the orange juice.

Replace the top layer of cake and spread it right to the edge with the remaining cream. Arrange the saved strawberries on the cream and surround the cake with sprigs of red-currants.

STRAWBERRY JELLY TART

A good, fruity summer party dish.

Short crust pastry (see page 176) or ready-made puff pastry
at least $\frac{1}{2}$ kilo (1 lb) strawberries
$\frac{1}{4}$ of a strawberry jelly
a little double cream

Roll out the pastry very thinly and line an 20cm (8-inch) pie tin

Prick all over with a fork and bake 'blind': line with a double layer of
tissue paper, fill with dried beans or such and bake in a pre-heated oven,
middle shelf, at gas 6, 200C for 10 minutes. Carefully remove the beans
and then the paper and cook a further 10 minutes. Allow to become
completely cold.

Make up the jelly as directed on the packet and leave until cold but not
yet quite beginning to set. Meanwhile, wash the strawberries (see page
177) and hull.

When the jelly is cold, spread enough cream over the cold, cooked pastry
to waterproof it, and then pile in the strawberries.

Pour the jelly over the strawberries and refrigerate to set it. Eat fairly
soon in case the pastry becomes soft.

PARTY FRUITY OATCAKES

sugar-free Scottish oatcakes
strawberries, raspberries and red currants
a little whipped cream
(opt. a little red currant jelly for glaze)

Spread each oatcake with enough cream for you to be able to stick on one
or two halved strawberries, cut side down, a raspberry or two and a few
plump red currants.

To make the glaze: put the jelly into a small saucepan and melt over a very
low heat. As soon as it's pourable, use a pastry brush to dab it over the
fruit to glaze it.

Other fruits such as blueberries, loganberries or blackberries can also be
used, but avoid fruits which must be cut, such as peaches, unless they are
coated at once with glaze, or they will turn brown.

CHOCOLATE SAUCE

1 bar dark chocolate – at least 70% cocoa solids
1-2 tbls. water
$^1/_2$ tsp. sunflower oil

Break up the chocolate and put it into a small bowl with the oil and water,
and stand it over a saucepan of boiling water. Try not to stir it or the
chocolate could dry, but you could push pieces of chocolate down as they
melt. When a knife slides easily through a piece of chocolate, it's done.
Stir, and use at once.

Very dark chocolate is much less sweet, so a good foil for fruit – and is
also less likely to cause over-indulgence. Chocolate with 99% cocoa
solids is now available and would be a good choice.

APPLE PIE

Everybody loves a good apple pie. This one is terrific – and let a child help with the decorations. Serve it slightly warm for the best flavour, on its own or with a good strong Cheddar cheese. With cream, it's nectar of the gods!

pastry as on page 176

1 kilo (2 lbs) cooking apples

cornflour or arrowroot

sugar

a handful of sultanas

cinnamon

freshly grated nutmeg

Line a 22cm (8-inch) pie tin with thinly rolled out pastry, and cover the pastry with a thin sprinkling of sieved cornflour. Wash the apples (no need to peel), core, and slice them thinly, a few at a time as you build the pie.

Make about 4 even layers of overlapping apple slices, scattering sultanas, sieved cornflour, sugar and pinches of cinnamon and nutmeg between the layers. Make a final extra layer in the centre to give the pie a mounded shape.

Cover with pastry, seal and crimp the edges and cut a hole or two for steam to escape. Decorate with pastry leaves, 'berries', a tassel and so on. Brush all over with milk, sprinkle with sugar and bake.

To bake: Put a shelf half way up the oven or very slightly above. Place a baking sheet on this shelf and then preheat the oven for about 10 minutes at gas 6-7, 210C.

Place the apple pie on the hot baking sheet, bake for 25 minutes, and then look to see if the pie is golden brown. If it isn't, bake a few minutes more. If your pie tin is such that the filling is very deep, the pie will need more cooking, so loosely cover the top with foil or greaseproof paper, lower the heat slightly and continue cooking. The pie is done when it smells lusciously and irresistibly of good old-fashioned, home-made apple pie.

To make a tassel: In a strip of pastry measuring 12cm by 3cm, make little cuts all down one long side. The cuts should be about $2\frac{1}{2}$cm long and about 4-5mm apart. Roll up the strip, lightly squeezing together the uncut part. Push this end into a hole in the centre of the pie.

THE BEST SCONES

An easy 'starter' recipe for children to make. Use 81% flour or a mixture of wholemeal and white. This recipe makes nine scones.

225g (8 oz) flour	pinch salt
30g (1 oz) caster sugar	30g (1 oz) currants
3 slightly heaped tsps. baking powder	60g (2 oz) butter milk and sugar for glazing
7 tbls. milk	

Sift the flour with the salt and baking powder. Rub the fat into the flour by hand or in a food processor. Stir in the sugar.

Make a soft dough with the milk, then mix in the currants. Roll out *thickly* to about 1 cm ($^1/_2$ -inch) thickness. If the dough is thin, the scones won't rise well.

Cut out about 9 scones and place on a greased baking sheet. Brush the tops with milk then sprinkle on a little sugar. Bake on the second shelf down from the top at gas 7, 210C for 12 minutes.

Cool a little on a wire rack and then eat as soon as cool enough, at any rate the same day, with butter and absolutely NO margarine. Good with a tangy jam as a treat, and surprisingly good with marmalade. You can re-warm them briefly in a cool oven or under a grill, but microwaving will toughen them.

Cheese scones:
Omit the sugar and fruit. Instead, add 2 oz grated, strongly-flavoured Cheddar cheese (or a mixture of Parmesan and Gruyère), a pinch of black pepper and a tiny pinch of cayenne pepper. You could dust the tops lightly with sieved paprika for an attractive finish.

CHRISTMAS PUDDING

This recipe makes almost 3 kilos (6 lb) of pudding, so you can make a large, 2 kilo (4 lb) one plus a smaller one perhaps for New Year (or even for Easter!) or for a present for someone. If you make three 1 kilo (2 lb) puddings, you could save one for *next* Christmas – and strictly speaking, puddings should be left to mature for a year. Alternatively of course, you could halve the recipe. Using boil-proof, plastic basins with snap-on lids saves a lot of work and fuss.

$\frac{1}{2}$ kilo (1 lb) raisins
250g ($\frac{1}{2}$ lb) currants
250g ($\frac{1}{2}$ lb) sultanas
a 400g sliced wholemeal loaf
60g (2 oz) plain wholemeal flour
$\frac{1}{2}$ nutmeg, grated
1 level tsp. mixed spice
1 tbl. black treacle
3 small eggs
1 tsp. salt

250g (8 oz) sugar
large lemon, grated/squeezed
large orange, grated/squeezed
115g (4 oz) apples, grated
115g (4 oz) carrot, grated
250g (8 oz) shredded suet
30g (1 oz) chopped almonds
115g (4 oz) chopped peel
$\frac{1}{2}$ bottle Guinness
$\frac{1}{2}$ tsp. baking powder

Make the loaf, crusts and all, into breadcrumbs in a food processor. Mix all the ingredients in column one together in a very large bowl.

Mix the ingredients in column two together in another bowl and then combine the two mixtures – and wish! (Don't even think of putting coins or whatnot into the mixture; they can cause serious accidents.)

Oil your pudding basins lightly and fill, packing the pudding mixture down well, leaving about 2-3cm at the top of each basin. Cover tightly.

Put into a steamer or into large pans of water, with the water coming about three quarters of the way up the basins. Cover tightly and boil steadily; big puddings need all of 6 hours, small ones 5.

Don't let your pan boil dry! And if the water goes off the boil, the puddings won't be cooking. Keep setting your kitchen timer, and top up with boiling water. When they are done, let them cool in the water.

Next day, either store the puddings in their basins or wrap them in double (non PVC) cling film or in tightly sealed food bags. Keep them in a cool, dark place (not the fridge or freezer) to mature until needed.

At Christmas, re-boil your pudding in its basin for 2-3 hours until it is black and sumptuous looking. If you do this on Christmas Eve it frees a gas ring on Christmas day. You can then easily reboil the pudding or microwave it briefly again on Christmas Day while the first course is being eaten.

RUM SAUCE

Even children can enjoy this mild rum sauce – while adults add more rum to it and perhaps have rum butter as well!

300ml ($\frac{1}{2}$ pint) of milk
I heaped tbl. cornflour
a dessertspoon of brown sugar
tiny pinch salt
a dash of dark rum

Mix the cornflour with a little of the milk while you heat the rest. Stir the hot milk into the cornflour paste. Return all to the saucepan and stir over a medium heat, to a thickened sauce. Mix in the sugar, salt and rum and pour into a jug. Place a disc of greaseproof paper on the sauce to prevent a skin forming. Reheat in a microwave oven.

MINCEMEAT

An excellent recipe for making with children and the best mincemeat recipe I know. Fruity, just spicy enough and not overly sweet. It will keep a year in well-sealed jars, preserved with the sugar and alcohol, so you could make enough for two years!

2 large juicy lemons.
1 kilo (2 lbs) mixed dried fruit
250g (8 oz) chopped citron peel
60g (2 oz) blanched, chopped almonds
180-225g (6-8 oz) Demerara sugar
175g (6 oz) shredded suet
2 tsps. mixed spice
1 tsp. cinnamon
1 tsp. freshly grated nutmeg
250g (8 oz) cooking apple
8 tbls. brandy, rum or whisky

Grate the rind of the lemons, squeeze the juice and put into a bowl. Stir in the citron peel, almonds, sugar, suet and spices. Wash and core the apple and put through a mincer or food processor with about a quarter of the dried fruit. Tip into the bowl along with the alcohol and the remaining fruit and mix well. Pack down into clean, dry jars; don't leave any air spaces. Screw the lids on tightly and store in a cool place until needed. This recipe makes about 2 kilos (4 lbs).

INDEX OF RECIPES

NOTES

THE END